Place
of
Quiet
Waters

Place
of
Quiet
Waters

By Margaret McIntyre

Longmans
Canada Limited

Printed in Canada
by T. H. Best Printing Company Limited, Don Mills, Ont.

Contents

Chapter 1

EACH SPRING, as the nomadic habits of our forebears begin to waken vague stirrings in the blood, most people experience that atavistic urge which varies in intensity with the thickness of the sufferer's civilized veneer—a sudden longing to get away from it all.

That memorable spring when I was attacked in full force by the urge, I was one of two career women sharing a city apartment; a member of that vast army of unhappy beings who are blasted out of their sleep each morning by the clang of an alarm clock, and who crawl automatically into their clothes with sleep-glued eyes and swallow their breakfasts spurred on by a feverish radio announcer giving out the latest thing in international crises punctuated by frequent reminders of the correct time.

Having been one of those curious anomalies known as a "career woman" long enough for any glamour that might be connected with the term to have evaporated completely, my one idea at this time was to escape from the wheel, and the result was a mind filled with revolt, and a bookcase spilling over with stories of rugged souls who had scooped a living out of the polar ice, hobnobbed with head-hunters in the South Seas, and paddled round the world in canoes.

The coming of spring with its insidious whisperings put a climax to my discontent, and one day I informed Jerry, with whom I shared a large apartment and a small bank account, that I was going to run away.

"You've been reading too many of those books," she said, eyeing the latest addition to my library, the jacket of which depicted a grinning green Eskimo driving a dog team round a towering blue iceberg. "You can't run away. Where would you go and what about your career?"

I thought about my career. It had commenced with high hopes and expensive study at a European conservatory of music and had ended up in complete disillusionment and a twelve-foot cell into which came a morbid procession of children every week to be instructed in the art of music. In this private torture chamber I spent several hours a day, and in between listening to Czerny's exercises rattled up and down the piano and the squeaking of tormented fiddles in the grip of sticky and resentful hands, I tried to explain the law of accidentals and the difference between the melodic and harmonic minors to children whose ancestors had seemingly been mentally deficient for the last six generations.

"I wouldn't call trying to teach Bach to teen-agers with a beat complex a career exactly. I can think of much pleasanter ways of spending one's life. How about you?"

Jerry looked grim. To her, a career meant an existence surrounded by office desks, pounding typewriters, black coffee and ulcerated executives, and her day usually ended in her joining me in a collapsed condition in front of the fire, where we listened to more international crises on the radio and struggled with the household budget. Between musing on the horrible state of the world and the equally horrible state of our finances, we considered the futility of life.

"Running away won't solve anything," she replied after a while. "Every spring you get some crazy idea like this and it never works out. Have you forgotten that February two or three years ago when you had the bright idea of driving across Canada in a broken-down

2

old heap and we ended up in the mountains with four flat tires and a busted piston rod?"

Vivid and uncomfortable memories floated through my mind.

"I remember all right. It was below zero and we hadn't brought any below-zero clothing with us. There wasn't a service station for miles. The nearest thing to life I saw was a steer lying in a field with all four feet in the air, and that was deader than a dodo."

Jerry assumed the highly virtuous air which means that she is right and I am wrong. "See what I mean? If it hadn't been for that truckload of Indians coming along we could have frozen to death out there."

I looked at her, the picture of righteousness, sitting with her feet on the fender, and decided to do a little reminiscing of my own.

"Have you forgotten that spring when you decided to buy a thirty-four-foot West Coast troller and go in for commercial fishing? You know how *that* little venture turned out."

Jerry broke in hastily. "I know! I know! Don't remind me. If it hadn't been for that fish packer spotting us, we could have been drowned. And if you're going to keep dragging up past mistakes, just remember that raspberry ranch we bought, and just when the berries were ripe for picking, the rain came and turned them all into jam and we went broke. It's no wonder we never have any money in the bank. Besides we're getting too old for this kind of nonsense. Your fortieth birthday is staring you in the face and mine has already kissed me good-bye. It's time we settled down."

But as time went on and the spring air grew more heady, I became more and more obsessed with the idea of getting away from it all. I never lost an opportunity of goading my reluctant partner into realizing the utter waste of a life spent shut up in an office, and the frustration of trying to cram music into children who were totally incapable of recognizing B flat from a bull's foot.

"Just take a look at these bills," I said after one session of frenzied finance when we had discovered that the net result of our month's labours had ended in nothing but an overdraft at the bank. "Income tax. Licence for the car. Licences for the dogs. Rent for the apart-

3

ment. Rent for my studio. Cleaner's bills, laundry, fuel, light, tele-phone, groceries. My God! It's simply ridiculous. There must be a different way of living than this."

"There isn't," replied Jerry in despondent tones. "Modern civili-zation won't allow you to live differently. Life these days has become simply a matter of digging the ditch to get the money to buy the bread to give you the strength to dig the ditch."

"If there isn't a better way of living than that," I said, "life doesn't have any meaning at all. Now if we only had a farm where we could grow our own food, and live a healthy outdoor life . . ." I leaned my elbows on the table and gazed into a romantic dream world where sharps and flats were miraculously transformed into buttercups and daisies. "A little brown farm-house with fields and a barn full of hay and wallflowers growing under the windows and a rooster crowing in the morning. Why can't we have something like that?"

"The reason we can't is because we don't know anything about farming," retorted Jerry.

"That's no reason at all. There has to be a first time for every-thing. There was a time when I had never given a music lesson, but I am doing it now."

"That's different. You were trained for that, but you were never trained for a farm life, and if you think teaching music is bad, just try working for a man who insists on combining stomach ulcers with mustard pickles. Besides, I've told you before, it's time we settled down."

Unconvinced, I reminded her that life, according to some people, was supposed to begin at forty, which remark was received with complete and disapproving silence.

In previous years my restless urges had usually died along with the jonquils and primroses, but this year they stayed with me long after spring had turned into summer. As the months passed, my seething restlessness began to communicate itself to Jerry and I began to hear dark murmurs concerning the horrors of an office job and the impossible tempo of modern life. The climax came one day

4

when she hurled herself into the studio, where I was watching the contortions of a pupil who was endeavouring to scratch his nose without removing his hands from the piano keys.

"How long are you going to be?" she mouthed silently behind the victim's back. I made a reassuring grimace in reply and turned to rescue a Chopin valse from the fate of slow assassination.

"Don't keep ducking your head like that, Jackie," I scolded irritably. "Take your hands off the keyboard. The notes aren't going to run away if you let go, and by the way, did you do *any* practising at all this week?"

"No!" replied Jackie with a triumphant leer.

"Why not? Don't you like the piano?"

"I hate it."

I probed patiently on. "Why bother taking lessons then?"

"My mom says it's good for me."

I mentally counted up to ten and then answered with exemplary self-control. "Just tell your mom to see that you practise for at least an hour every day or else not to send you back for any more lessons."

I opened the door and Jackie took a sullen departure, scuffing his feet along the floor and trailing his music case by the strap.

"Jeezels!" I leaned up against the door in a state of utter exhaustion. "I think I'll try scrubbing floors for a living."

Jerry eyed me darkly. "Let me know if you need an assistant. I've been thinking about that farm idea of yours all the way home, and the more I think about it the better it looks. At least barns don't have air conditioners that break down."

I looked at her curiously.

"And just what is all this leading up to?"

"I'm going to run away."

"Well, well, well," I replied with mounting sarcasm. "Look who's talking! *You* told *me* it couldn't be done."

Jerry shrugged her shoulders.

"I've changed my mind. I think it can. I've come to the conclusion that all this high-powered, press-button style of living is wrong. We should go to some place where there aren't any people or pianos

5

or peptic ulcers and live like Indians or Eskimos or something uncomplicated like that."

My mind reeled groggily for a moment, weighing the relative merits of teepee and igloo, and an answering enthusiasm began to rise in me.

"Are you really serious?"

Jerry looked at me with solemnly raised hand. "Absolutely. Instead of working ourselves into an early grave earning money to buy food and clothes and unnecessary luxuries, let's try getting back to nature. Raise our own food; make our own clothes; hunt and fish and that sort of thing. We will be healthy, happy and solvent all at the same time, which will be an entirely new experience for us." She thought for a minute, then went on.

"Surely we can save enough money to last us until we get organized, and if it works out, it may be the beginning of the kind of life we have always wanted, and if it doesn't work out—well, we can always come back and be civilized again."

"Of course," I answered, my spirits rising sky high. "But it's bound to work out. There really isn't anything to it. Any fool can fire a gun, and catching fish is only a matter of dropping a hook and line into the sea; and if you put seeds into the ground they turn into vegetables and there you are."

"Ye-es." Jerry chewed her fingertips thoughtfully. "I rather think there's more to it than that. Our new office manager goes fishing every week-end, but I never knew him to catch any fish. His wife says that with all the money he spends on equipment and boats and guides, she could buy enough fish to feed all the undeveloped people in the world for the rest of their lives."

"He can't go to the right places then. There are lakes up North where the fish are shouldering each other out of the water, and the game comes up and begs to be shot. That's where we should go."

Jerry looked at me warily.

"Just a minute. Let's not get too ambitious. I said I wanted to get away from it all, but not *that* far away." She frowned thoughtfully. "We'll need to stay within reach of transportation of some sort.

6

After all, there are lots of things we can't produce, like tea and sugar and stuff."

"The thing to do," I said briskly, "is to take plenty of supplies to wherever we are going and gradually cut down on our civilized feeding habits till we can do without them."

"All right! First things first. Where *are* we going?"

A profound discussion which explored all the possibilities of arctic outposts and South Sea islands came to an end after a somewhat shattering examination of our bank-book.

"Listen," protested Jerry, who was the financial brains of the partnership, "South Pacific islands are OUT. Only a Texas oilman could afford to pioneer in a place like that. Real estate is sold by the inch and besides, they must be civilized up to the neck by now. We'll have to think of something else."

I sat down on the piano stool, rested my elbows with a resounding crash on the piano keys, dropped my chin into my hands, and thought hard.

"Somehow an island sounds so romantic. A small private kingdom surrounded by acres of sea."

Jerry brightened up.

"I know. Let's buy an island in the *North* Pacific. There are lots of them on the map. Uninhabited and everything, just waiting for someone to come and live on them. A man in the office was telling me you can buy them from the Government for next to nothing. They call it a Crown grant or something. We have got lots of maps at home. Let's look at them tonight and get some idea of the geography of this coast."

The next few days were filled with ecstatic plannings as we pored over maps and charts. A two-week vacation that came due at this time gave us the opportunity we needed to set out on our search for the Elysian Fields.

Our exploring, by coastal steamer, led us up the shores of northern British Columbia, a wild and rugged land ceaselessly charged by an ill-named Pacific Ocean and fringed with a border of islands and inlets. Islands whose rocky shores were licked smooth by the constant surge of the sea, and whose peaks were awhirl with the beating wings of seabirds. Inlets whose mountain-shadowed waters were deep and sunless.

The steamer was large, and the few passengers consisted mainly of lumbermen clad in lively-coloured shirts and mackinaws and wearing heavy calked logging boots. In between studying our fellow passengers, we looked at the scenery with awe. There were towering mountains smeared with the remains of the winter's snow. Waterfalls tumbled like silver threads down their craggy sides and lost themselves in the thick forests below. In some places the shore-line was steep and the rocks took on grotesque shapes—a series of leviathan organ pipes or what looked like the pillars of an ancient temple. The resemblance between the handiwork of man and that of nature was striking at times.

Occasionally there would be a little bay where the immense forest trees swept down to the water's edge, and in a small clearing scratched out of the forest we could see a shabby little wooden hut with a crooked stove-pipe protruding from the sagging roof.

Our eager inquiries of the crew usually gave us the information that they were abandoned trappers' huts.

"There seems to be nobody living in any of them," said Jerry, looking at the desolate landscape.

"Perhaps they met with an accident and died because nobody could get to them," I suggested, beginning to think better of our comfortable apartment in the city.

"Not likely," replied the crew man easily. "They often move to new locations when the trap lines run out."

"One location seems to be as bad as another," I said. "I never saw such wild country. Even the names of the places give me the horrors. Just look at this map. Grief Point. Desolation Sound. Wreck Bay, and all those rapids with the funny names tearing about. Anyone choosing to live in places like these would be a plain fool."

The crew man leaned his arms on the steamer rail and looked over the side at the water rushing past.

"There's some folk that wouldn't live anywhere else," he said.

8

"Take that long inlet we passed just now. There's an old guy lives up at the head all by himself. He owns some mining claims in there and spends all his time puttering up and down the mountains looking for gold. He's been in there for thirty years and he's had his feet frostbit and he's been clawed by grizzlies and he's never found the gold. He's over seventy now and wild horses wouldn't drag him out."

"How does he manage about supplies?" I asked, intrigued in spite of myself.

"He has a row-boat. Supplies are delivered to one of the camps and once a month he rows down to the mouth of the inlet, six miles or more, and collects them."

"Supposing he was sick or had an accident?"

The sailor straightened himself up leisurely.

"If he didn't show up for a couple of months, some of the men at the camp would likely go down and see why."

"But he could be dead by then!" I exclaimed in horror.

"Sure he could; and knowing old Nels, I reckon that's the way he would want to die. Out in the wilds by himself instead of in some fancy hospital with a lot of quacks cutting him up and sticking their fingers in his insides. There's lots like him up here."

The sailor wandered away, leaving us to meditate on his words. The little farm with the wallflowers and the rooster seemed a far cry from this sort of rugged pioneering.

Now and then the steamer came to a stop at a wharf belonging to a logging community, and we leaned over the rail to look at the collection of rough unpainted sheds and houses, the logging equipment, and the rough roads leading up into the scarred mountainside. Sometimes, on account of the steepness of the shore-line, the scanty population lived in float houses on the water. Whole colonies of these little houses were mounted on log booms with runways leading up to the land, and on the platforms surrounding the dwellings women were hanging out their washing on improvised clothes-lines. Children were playing, oblivious of the deep water all around, and far up the mountains where the men were working, we heard the clatter of giant tractors and the crash of great trees interspersed with the shrieks of the donkey man's steam whistle.

It was in these places that our fellow passengers began to leave us. Shouldering their kit-bags, they lumbered ashore, a picturesque and integral part of the Canadian scene.

There were other stops too, for "boat landings." This meant that the steamer had to heave to in the middle of the sea while two or three small boats came bobbing out to meet us. The occupants were generally residents from one of the deep fjords which was out of the steamer's track. Looking down at them from the upper deck and watching them struggling to keep their boats from bumping against the side of the steamer, we pondered this strange new way of life. Supplies and mail were thrown into the waiting boats and an occasional passenger lowered himself with the utmost nonchalance along with them; then, after exchanging a few pleasantries with the crew, the rowers pulled away to commence their lonely trip back to their hidden homesteads.

As the stops for freight and passengers became fewer, the scenery became more forbidding and the inlets and islands more numerous.

"Islands! Look at them!" I exclaimed, almost falling over the rail in my excitement. "Islands everywhere. How about one of these?"

The member of the crew who was our self-appointed guide gave me a sidelong look and spat contemptuously into the sea.

"Sure," he replied laconically. "Islands everywhere and not a drop of water on any of 'em."

"Water?" I echoed, somewhat dashed. "There seem to be people living on some of them. What do they do for water?"

"Trap water from the roof mostly, and in dry weather they pack it in barrels from the mainland."

"Oh come on, let's go back to town," I said, my pioneering spirit quailing before this prospect.

Jerry gave me a stony glance. "No," she said, "we are going through with this, and we will look for an island with water on it. Water is the first essential when you are looking for a camp site. I read that in a Boy Scout manual once, and I noticed that all those logging communities had big streams running down the mountain-side close to them."

"Yes, but they were all on the mainland," I objected. "I can't see any streams on these little islands."

"We'll have to find a big island then, one big enough to hold a mountain and a stream. You don't expect to find just what you want right away."

"If you're wise," said the deck-hand, who had been listening with a sardonic grin, "you won't go looking for any desert islands up here. If you are so set on this nutty idea, you will choose one of the big inhabited islands. Some are big enough to get lost on, and the few people living there won't bother you if you don't bother them. Likely you'll never even see 'em. They hide in the bush and if anyone comes calling uninvited they generally shoot first and say 'Howdy' afterwards."

"Sounds real neighbourly," I said dolefully. "I think I would rather have an island of my own, even with no water."

Our first trip in search of islands was not successful, nor was the second or third. In fact, it was some time before we located an island that seemed to meet with all our requirements, and then it was through a newspaper advertisement which offered acreage for sale in the island-haunted region which we had already visited.

A letter of inquiry brought back a reply couched in ungrammati-cal and ill-spelt English which invited us to visit the owners, prom-ised overnight accommodation, and volunteered the information that all steamers would be "met."

Our recent trips up the coast had fully acquainted us with the hazards of "boat landings," so the latter remark left us under no illusions as to what to expect.

"That means there is no wharf for the steamer to tie up to and we shall have to climb down into a small boat from the freight deck and row ashore," I said. "At least, this man—I can't make out what his name is, the writing is so bad. It looks like a foreign name of some kind. He will be expecting us, so there will be no danger of our getting shot."

We lost no time in checking boat schedules, packing a bag, and setting out again on our search for islands.

The long journey up the ragged coast-line brought us at last to our destination, a large green oasis sleeping on a sun-drenched sea at the mouth of a deep mountain-shaded fjord.

"There you are," said our friendly deck-hand. "There's your island and God help you."

"How do we get to it?" I inquired uneasily.

The sailor pointed out to where several boats were bobbing about in the sea, and as the steamer slowed down, they all converged on us.

"Islanders coming out for mail," explained the man. "Better get down to the freight deck if you're going ashore."

Jerry and I picked up our bags and followed our guide down to the freight deck, whose massive doors were thrown back, framing a picture of racing white-crested waves and wallowing boats against a backdrop of green tree-lined shore.

The steamer, now at a standstill and heaving gently up and down, turned to form a lee for the small boats surging towards her. We stood among the piles of crates and baggage, surrounded by the assorted smells of fish and rotting vegetables, and watched the different-sized craft struggling towards the steamer through the waves.

I took the letter from my purse and showed it to one of the sailors.

"Do you know this man?" I said. "He is supposed to meet us."

The sailor glanced at the signature and laughed.

"Everybody knows him."

"What's he like?"

The sailor laughed again. "Just like a lot of other ruddy bastards that live in these places. What do you want with him?"

"He says he has some land for sale," I replied hesitantly.

The man turned aside to move a coil of rope. "He could have, at that. He owns a couple of hundred acres. Just watch your step, that's all. Some of these guys would steal the tail feathers from an angel."

A sturdily built skiff slid up below the open doors of the freight deck; a pair of brown muscular hands gripped the door sill and the head and shoulders of the boatman rose up in the opening and peered within.

"Two passengers for you, Keijo," said the sailor.

We stepped forward shyly and found ourselves looking down into a lean, dour face out of which stared a pair of the coldest blue eyes I had ever seen.

"How do you do?" I said uncertainly.

The eyes scanned me from head to foot in silence, noting all the details of my beige tailored suit and wolf-trimmed top-coat, and with an expression of the utmost contempt stared at my rakish hat; then, with an unintelligible grunt, he beckoned us towards him.

While he held the skiff steady, the members of the crew helped us down into it. Our bags were thrown unceremoniously in after us, and without a word Keijo picked up the oars and commenced pulling strongly for the shore.

"We should have worn slacks," I muttered, lifting the hem of my skirt out of the dirty salt water that sloshed about under the floor boards.

"And sea boots," added Jerry, looking ruefully at her salt-stained oxfords.

Huddled in the stern, we made attempts at conversation with Keijo, all of which were met with grunts and monosyllables. At last, despairing of getting any intelligible answers to our questions, we gave up and concentrated all our attention on the island which we were rapidly approaching.

As we drew nearer, we saw that the shore-line was a mighty bastion of solid rock topped with tall pointed firs. There was no sign of habitation. The other boats had all disappeared in the direction of other islands and inlets, and the only other living things besides ourselves were the seagulls which whirled overhead with forlorn cries.

We looked in vain for a beach on which to land, but all that met our eyes was tall frowning cliffs against which the surf beat relentlessly.

I questioned the grim unsmiling man in the bows.

13

"I don't see any houses. Where do you live?"

There was no answer. His stony blue eyes flickered over us once and then returned to their contemplation of the horizon.

"Nice old mess you've got us into," I growled in Jerry's ear. "You and your islands!"

As we gradually came towards the shore, Keijo ceased rowing for a moment, turned and looked over his shoulder and pointed to the land. Following the direction of his hand, we saw an opening in the cliffs, and in a few minutes the incoming tide had floated us into a narrow rock-walled canyon. So close were the sides that there was no room for two boats to pass. The smooth walls towered above our heads shutting out the light, and the dark waters sucked and thundered in hollow echoes at their base.

We stiffened involuntarily and I clutched the side of the boat in momentary panic. Keijo, using one oar as a paddle, peered intently over the side for hidden rocks as the pent-up water swept us through the channel. Bubbles of brownish froth and little whirlpools eddied around us; now and then a rocky ledge showed clearly through the water, or an ugly jagged point came dangerously close to the keel of the boat. Keijo's skilful use of the paddle avoided these rocky hazards and the boat was swung and manoeuvred between them with the ease that comes with long familiarity.

Then the forbidding walls fell away and we emerged from the dark cavern with its sullen waters and thunderous echoes into a wide and peaceful lagoon—a place of such calm beauty that we gasped with astonishment.

It was fully two miles in length and more than half as wide, and it stretched like a mirror between banks of forest trees and low moss-grown cliffs. At the head, facing us as we floated in, a range of snow-capped mountain peaks on the mainland behind reared proudly into a windy sky and was reflected faithfully in the calm waters of the lagoon.

"How lovely!" I whispered, all my apprehensions fading away as I took in the details of this hidden paradise. Across the water on a pebbly beach, a colony of gulls squabbled noisily. A blue heron raised itself from the shallows as the boat passed, and with a harsh cry and a great flapping of wings, sailed away over the trees.

I touched Jerry's elbow. "It's too good to be true."

Rounding a slight bend in the lagoon, we came upon a small bay on the shores of which were a collection of dun-coloured wooden buildings. The ground around them had been cleared of forest and an orchard of pink and white fruit blossom frothed gaily against a background of sombre firs. Thickly wooded mountains in serrated ranks rose behind the little homestead, and down a cleft in the rocks a mountain torrent tumbled into the sea.

"Water!" declared Jerry in tones of satisfaction.

Keijo's eyes fastened on us briefly, but he made no comment. Instead, he pulled the boat up to a primitive floating wharf, secured the painter, and stepping out, walked in silence up the runway leading to the shore, leaving us to follow or not as we wished.

We looked at his retreating back.

"What are we supposed to do now?" queried Jerry in annoyed tones.

I crawled stiffly to my feet. "Evidently this is the terminus. Come on, let's get out."

Stepping carefully onto the rickety wharf, we followed Keijo's back up the runway, over the pebbles which lined the beach, through the wet grass growing wild under the foamy apple blossom, and up to the door of the main building.

Here we stopped. Keijo had disappeared inside, and we heard him speaking to someone in an unfamiliar tongue. A minute later a fat, jolly-looking woman appeared in the doorway, greeted us with a broad smile, and in strongly accented English invited us to enter.

We walked in, casting covert glances around. The house seemed to consist of three rooms. The one into which the door opened was a combined kitchen, living- and dining-room, spotlessly clean but completely bare of all furnishings except for a large wood-burning stove, a deep fuel box and a kitchen table and chairs. The windows were curtainless but framed a breath-taking view of mountain and sea. Doors on two sides of the room led, one into a bedroom, the other into a long glassed-in sun porch. As we entered, we could see Keijo's back disappearing again through the sun-porch door.

The woman drew chairs out from the table, put the kettle on to boil, then, sitting down opposite to us, broke into a flow of eager talk.

Bit by bit we discovered that she and her husband Keijo, to whom she never referred by any name other than "he," were Finlanders, and together with their Danish hired man, lived alone on their homestead. They had cows, chickens, and boats, and they fished, grew their own produce, manufactured their own electric light from the waterfall beside the house, and in general seemed to have solved the problem of living without money.

"That is just what we would like to do," I said when she paused for breath. "Whereabouts is this land you have for sale?"

The woman cast a glance towards the sun porch, lowered her voice and said, "*He* will showing it to you after you are eating."

Supper, at which neither Keijo nor the hired man appeared, was spread on the bare boards of the kitchen table, and consisted of freshly caught salmon, fresh garden vegetables, home-made bread, farm butter, new milk, and a fruit pudding.

"Boy, I never tasted anything like this in my life," said Jerry, buttering her fourth slice of bread and refilling her mug with the milk. "Do you grow all this stuff yourself?"

Our hostess beamed a proud assent.

"Sounds like a lot of work to me," I commented ruefully, "but I suppose with a couple of men to do the heavy work, it isn't so bad."

Keijo's wife looked at me, her blue eyes wide with amazement.

"I am doing the heavy work," she said. "*He* too busy."

"What does *he* do?" I inquired pointedly, but Keijo's wife seemed a little vague about this, and the well-timed entrance of Keijo himself prevented any further indiscreet inquiries.

After supper was over, Keijo demonstrated his ability to speak passably good English when it suited his purpose. On hearing of our plans to begin a new life, he nodded his head in approval and proceeded to deliver himself of a dissertation on the evils of civilization and the high moral value of life lived "the hard way," as he termed it.

In a few terse mispronounced words and with a face absolutely devoid of any expression, he gave us to understand that life, according to his philosophy, was intended to be a thoroughly uncomfortable business. It consisted of working from dawn till dark, pleasure of any kind being taboo and only the barest essentials for daily living allowed.

"Is that the way people live in Finland?" inquired Jerry.

Keijo's face became more stony than before, and we soon discovered that when he was faced with a leading question, a sudden accession of obtuseness and an inability to understand English stood him in good stead.

"I taking you to see the land," he said, changing the subject.

We followed him down to the wharf. His wife made a move to accompany us, but a curt remark from Keijo in his own language halted her, and she stood in the flowery orchard watching us go, her face a little wistful.

In complete silence, Keijo rowed us down the lagoon again towards the cavernous entrance until we came to another little indentation in the shore-line. With a sudden strong jerk on the oars, he turned the boat in, ran it up on the beach and jumped out, motioning us to follow.

We climbed up a series of shelving rocks to a cleared mossy plateau in the middle of which stood a small one-roomed cabin. In splendid isolation it stood, its empty windows looking out across the water to the distant snow-clad mountains while the dark forest trees stood sentinel around it.

We looked inside. There were a small iron camp stove, two canvas cots, and a wooden table and chairs.

We walked back outside and stood on the edge of the bluff overlooking the lagoon. It had been a day of hot sunshine and intoxicating scents were rising from the moss and evergreens. A gentle wind stirred the tree-tops and rippled the surface of the lagoon, causing a soft lap-lap of the waves on the beach below. All about us was a great sense of peace, primitive and absolute.

"What is the name of this place?" I asked dreamily.

"It having Indian name," said Keijo gruffly. "It meaning Place of Quiet Waters."

"Place of Quiet Waters," I echoed. "How perfectly true."

With an effort we tore ourselves away from the enchanted scene and followed Keijo over an overgrown trail and up the hillside to inspect the rest of the property, most of which was rock and almost vertical.

Farther back from the sea, the ground levelled off to a stand of alder which Keijo assured us would when cleared make excellent ground for vegetables. Behind that again was a small lake formed by a dammed-up stream, from which water could be obtained. The price seemed reasonable; furthermore, Keijo was willing for us to stay in the cabin for a couple of days until the steamer made its return trip to town, and look the place over thoroughly before definitely committing ourselves.

Already convinced that this was the only place in the world for us, we returned to Keijo's homestead to collect our bags and to buy a supply of food from his stores. He lent us a somewhat battered row-boat, warned us not to attempt to go outside the lagoon, and left us to our own devices.

The first thing we did, after changing into slacks and sweaters, was to disregard his warning, climb into the boat and head for the mysterious entrance, where we found that any attempt to get out of the lagoon meant certain suicide. As we approached the entrance, our ears were deafened by a hideous roaring, and standing up in the boat, we saw the whole channel filled with boiling white spume. Whirlpools spun madly between mountains of green water. The currents running this way and that forced fountains of froth up the sides of the canyon, and the whole channel presented a picture of complete horror.

"Rapids!" I groaned. "Holy Micmac!"

Checking with Keijo later, we discovered that only at certain times when the tide was slack was the passage navigable, and that once inside the lagoon, a person was completely marooned until the next change of tide, unless he owned a canoe and could boast Indian ancestry.

"We certainly won't be plagued with casual callers," said Jerry as we rowed back to the cabin.

Further explorings proved the rest of the lagoon to be completely safe. It was always calm, a timid sailor's paradise. We found it full of fascinating and obscure little coves where the steep rocks broke up into gravelly beaches. Here we could pull up the boat and leaving it in safety above the high-water mark, climb the shelving tables of rock until we reached a height from which we could survey the whole panorama of blue mountain ranges melting one behind the other into the distance, the white-capped sea tumbling outside the quiet lagoon, and the dense forests of fir. Around us little groves of jackpine and odd clumps of spirea and salal grew apparently out of the solid rock, and beneath our feet thick moss like shabby green velvet covered everything.

"This is what I have been looking for all my life," I said, gazing out at the ridges of mountains, and the forest crowding darkly along their sides. "Already I seem to have dropped a ton weight from my mind."

For the next two days we lived an idyllic existence. We woke in the morning to a cabin filled with sunshine and the scent of sea-wrack. We carried our drinking water down from the lake and cooked our meals over a fire of dry branches gathered in the forest behind the cabin. We spent lazy hours lying on the aromatic moss in the hot sunny afternoons, and at night we slept on the hard little cots with the cool sea wind blowing through the cracks in the boards and the great silence all about us.

Although Keijo studiously avoided us, his wife Sundi, on more than one occasion, rowed slowly past the isolated little cabin, casting hopeful and surreptitious glances upwards, and her eager response to our friendly hails gave evidence of her longing for feminine companionship.

From her we learnt that the island was thirty miles in length, and its few inhabitants, living in various inaccessible spots, were mostly fishermen. Owing to the complete lack of anything remotely resembling roads, all visiting had to be done by boat, and was largely dependent on weather conditions.

The only people living in the lagoon itself were Keijo, with his anti-social tendencies, and four brothers of the strong-and-silent persuasion, who owned a large tract of land at the head of the lagoon, engaged in logging operations, and kept very much to themselves.

We also discovered that the scanty population of the island had mostly drifted out here from various European countries, and that most of them preferred to speak their own language to wrestling with the complexities of the English tongue.

"Don't they speak English at all?" I asked, thinking sadly of my schoolroom French and few German phrases.

Sundi gave a fat chuckle.

"They speaking English when they having to," she said.

"If they live here, why don't they speak it all the time?" queried Jerry.

Sundi looked at us thoughtfully.

"If you are living in Finland, you are not speaking Finn to each other."

We thought over this unfamiliar viewpoint for a minute or two in silence before turning to more immediate matters.

"We will need a boat, won't we?" I asked.

Sundi's face brightened. It appeared that "he" had two boats which could be bought cheap.

"And about food?" I questioned further. "I suppose the mail steamer will bring in supplies?"

A furtive glance in the direction of the homestead, and an almost unconscious lowering of the voice as Sundi informed us that "he" disapproved of buying supplies of any description.

"He living off the land," said Sundi.

"Well, if we prefer to buy some of our groceries, it is really none of his business, is it?" I asked pleasantly.

"He thinking it great foolishness," said Sundi uneasily.

We had learnt by now that "great foolishness" was in Keijo's dictionary a term of the strongest condemnation. We shuddered.

"Of course," I capitulated helplessly, "we intend to plant vegetables and fish and hunt and all that sort of thing; but just at first, you know—till we get used to it . . ."

"He thinking it great foolishness," maintained Sundi, shaking her head.

The morning of the day on which the steamer made its return trip to town, Jerry and I set out to track down the elusive Keijo, and discovered him in a shed behind the house, stretching a deer hide on a frame. He looked up with an expressionless face as we entered, and then continued with his work as if we had not been there. On our informing his unresponsive back that we had decided to buy the land, he grudgingly stopped what he was doing. He led us into the house, grunted something to his wife, produced a writing tablet, a bottle of ink and a pen and sat down expectantly.

Jerry handed over a cheque for the amount previously mentioned, and received in exchange a scrawled acknowledgement and a rough description of metes and bounds. Sundi produced four glasses of home-made wine, the acidity of which nearly took the skin off our tongues, and we all gravely drank to the completion of the sale.

Before Keijo took us out to meet the south-bound steamer, we discussed with him the probable date of our return. Allowing six months to wind up our affairs, dispose of anything unnecessary to our new life and purchase articles which would be more in keeping with it, would bring us well into fall, at which time, Keijo claimed, the weather would be uncertain. There would be no dry fuel. The seas would be rough, and the unlined cabin unsuitable for winter living quarters.

We accordingly agreed to wait until the following spring before commencing our experiment in life lived "the hard way." We took a last rapturous look at our new property, and went back to town in a state of delirium to prepare for our adventure in pioneering.

Chapter 2

THE REACTIONS of our friends when we told them of our plans were definite.

"Are you out of your minds? Here you have both got good jobs and a comfortable home, and you mean to say that you are prepared to throw it all away and go up to a place like that? What on earth's got into you?"

"You wouldn't understand," I would reply loftily. "Material things aren't everything. My soul needs to grow."

The answer to this was usually a loud, derisive hoot, accompanied by some uncomplimentary remarks concerning the probable state of my soul both at present and in the future.

"Haven't you ever wanted to get away from it all?" I asked in a glow of exaltation left over from our recent holiday.

"Yes, of course. But people don't *do* things like this."

"Well, *we* do."

Ignoring the head-shakings and hand-wringings of our friends, we threw our respective careers to the winds and commenced a wild disposal of all unnecessary belongings.

"We will take all the furniture, of course," said Jerry, going the rounds of the apartment with paper and pencil. "We won't need the car, so we will sell it and use the money to buy tools and proper clothing and lumber for building and supplies of food, and—oh, loads of things. We can't begin collecting them too soon."

"I thought we were going to live like Indians," I objected. "They didn't have any furniture."

"Don't be silly," said Jerry. "We have got all this furniture, and we might as well take it along; there's no sense in being uncomfortable."

She continued her promenade round the room, taking notes.

"We can get rid of a lot of these pots and dishes, and we won't be needing the piano—we can sell that."

"Why?" I argued. "If we are going to take all the furniture, we might as well make a good job of it and take the piano."

Jerry stopped pacing the floor and looked at me.

"What on earth do you want the piano for? I thought you wanted to get away from all that kind of thing. Why not sell it and use the money for something sensible?"

"Like what?" I asked sullenly.

"Well—we might need snowshoes or skis or something."

"Listen," I said grimly, "I have never been on snowshoes or skis in all my life, and that piano cost over a thousand dollars. It's going with me."

"All right, all right," Jerry said in resigned tones, "but I don't know how you expect to drag a grand piano up there. However, you just go ahead and try."

Her face brightened as a sudden thought struck her. "Hey, it's not a bad idea at that! We'll take our violins too." She gave me a sidelong look. "Remember those few lessons you gave me once? I admit I sound as if someone stepped on the cat, but with lots of time to practise–who knows? I might turn into another Heifetz."

A series of expeditions to second-hand stores produced a collection of tools, the sight of which would have sent an experienced woodsman into a coma.

There was a seven-foot cross-cut saw, minus one handle and very rusty; a bucksaw, badly in need of setting; and a whole litter of smaller saws. We bought a broad-axe whose curved, murderous blade brought back faint reminiscences of the Tower of London. We also purchased the heaviest of sledge-hammers and wedges without having the least idea of their use; and we bought felling axes, planes and hammers and chisels, the proprietors of the different stores, scenting greenhorns and with a shrewd eye to business, having assured us that we would certainly need all of them if we intended to do any building.

A farewell dinner-party and presentation given by the members of Jerry's office staff increased our new belongings to the extent of two sets of oilskins and a huge draw-knife shaped like an Australian boomerang. Another farewell party, given by my pupils, ended with a gift of an old-fashioned oil lamp whose white china globe was painted over with monstrous pink roses.

"Shades of my grandmother!" exclaimed Jerry, eyeing it with a shudder. "Throw it away! I'd rather sit in the dark."

"You can't do that," I objected. "After all, they meant well, and we *do* need oil lamps."

"Not that kind. I'm going to buy some of these new Aladdin table lamps with parchment shades."

We had decided that when settled in our new home, we would buy a goat, thus solving the milk problem. A whole set of dairy equipment was purchased to take care of the gallons of milk which we fondly expected to obtain from her. There were enamel pails, glass churns, wooden butter pats, skimming ladles, and all the latest gadgets pertaining to the modern dairy.

To further prepare us for our new life, we practised bread-making in the tiny kitchenette of our apartment. The first attempts were disastrous, the dough either remaining in a sodden lump at the bottom of the pan, or else rising to such an extent that it had to be clawed off the walls. By dint of much perseverance on our part, and with the assistance and advice of our landlady, we at last managed to bring our bread-making safely past the stage where the results had to be smuggled out of the building along with the garbage, and to that pitch of perfection where it could be displayed to sceptical friends.

Emboldened by our success, we bought two quarts of cream and attempted to make butter in our new churn. We were somewhat dashed by the small amount which resulted, but it was undeniably butter and quite edible, which was more than could be said for the cheese which we manufactured out of the left-over buttermilk. This product of a laboriously followed recipe turned into a pallid, rubbery substance which tasted like wet flannel and had a quite indescribable perfume.

"It smells like something that has been dead for years," said Jerry, poking suspiciously at it with a fork. "You've certainly done it this time. Even a rat wouldn't eat it."

Most of our city clothes we gave away and replaced them with slacks, sweaters, overalls, heavy wool socks and strong footwear. A complete set of fishing tackle, a .22 rifle, and a large volume which guaranteed to supply us with information on everything from building a pigpen to embalming a corpse completed our purchases, and we felt ready for anything.

When our preparations were finally completed, our apartment had taken on the appearance of an overstocked auction room. Piles of crates and cartons were stacked up against the walls. Garden rakes, rolls of hog fencing, and fishing-rods fell out of every cupboard whenever the door was opened. Strange and uncitified garments were draped over the chairs, and getting into bed at night entailed a climb over a wheelbarrow, a small garden plough, and a square galvanized bathtub filled with flowerpots, ammunition and life-jackets.

"Anyone would think we were outfitting a polar expedition," said I, looking dubiously at the collection. "Just how complicated can the simple life get? I thought we were going to live like Indians, and here we have collected more stuff than we ever had."

"You can't live the simple life unless you are equipped for it," said Jerry irritably. "You have to have tools for gardening, and rods for fishing and guns for shooting and axes and saws for cutting down trees. It would be plain silly to go up there with nothing but a lot of furniture and a grand piano."

I shook my head doubtfully.

"Just wait till Keijo gets an eyeful of this—I don't think he is going to like it one bit."

With spring came the great removal.

This could never have been accomplished without the help of Keijo, who always made an annual trip to town at this time and in a burst of generosity, no doubt regretted later on, offered to bring up our effects on his boat.

"Have you a boat big enough to take furniture and things?" I had asked wonderingly.

"I am having freight boat," Keijo had replied proudly.

I opened my eyes wide at this piece of information.

"Why, that's wonderful! We can load all the things on it and bring the stuff right into the lagoon."

This had seemed to solve all our transportation problems, but at that time we had not seen Keijo's freight boat.

On the day of his arrival in town, we sallied down to the wharf with him to measure the cubic content of the ship's hold.

"Are you sure there will be room for all our stuff?" I asked diffidently as we walked down the ramp.

"There being plenty room," answered Keijo, blissfully ignorant of the apartment and its contents.

"How about my grand piano?" I inquired.

Keijo stopped in his tracks and faced me, his eyes like twin icebergs.

"Piano?" he echoed. "You taking piano?"

"Why not?" I asked belligerently.

"Great foolishness!" he remarked, and turning on his heel, resumed his march down the wharf. Jerry and I, with an exchange of dubious looks, followed more slowly.

When we reached the berth where the boat was moored, we pushed our way through the crowd of gapers standing beside it, and stood—stunned with horror.

26

Keijo's boats were all grisly creations of his own and we had seen samples of his handiwork on the island, but nothing that we had seen had prepared us for this particular sea-going nightmare.

Originally it had been a small down-at-heel freighter which he had picked up from a wrecking company and remodelled to suit his own ideas of what a boat should look like. The resulting effect in this case was rather as if someone had taken a large bite out of the stern and by way of compensation made an addition to the bows in the shape of something that looked like a four-room cottage complete with French doors and and verandah. Motive power was supplied by one decrepit diesel engine which ran in spasmodic gasps and one small gas engine which filled in the blanks left by the diesel.

The different-sized propellers protruding from the rear gave it a decidedly raffish appearance, and this was further increased by the paint job, which was an obvious conglomeration scraped from the bottom of numerous paint cans. The crowning touch was a contraption which resembled a large metal lamp shade dangling from the bows.

"What on earth's that?" I asked, pointing to it in bewilderment.

The wharfinger, who was standing beside me, stared stony-eyed in the direction of my pointing hand.

"That," he replied laconically, "is a mushroom anchor à la Keijo, and if you ask me the blasted boat's a damn monstrosity and shouldn't be allowed out."

I edged away and joined Jerry, who was still looking at the boat with an expression of utter disbelief.

"It looks as if the bottom would fall out of it if you loaded it with anything heavier than a toothbrush," she murmured. "I guess you had better leave your piano behind."

"I guess so," I replied unhappily. "In fact, I don't feel like risking *anything* on it, but it's too late to do anything about that now."

The next day was spent in loading our goods and chattels into the hold of the "monstrosity," aided by an army of furniture movers. Keijo kept gloomily aloof and eyed with ever increasing disapprobation the collection of articles which we had considered necessary to the simple life.

There were large overstuffed chairs, a chesterfield, a quantity of rugs, Chinese house mottoes framed in carved teakwood, tapestries, Chinese vases, coffee tables, occasional chairs, oil paintings, mirrors, tables, cushions, crates of books, and eight large crates of china, silver and linen. Besides all this frippery, there were all the tools and equipment we had purchased, plus three thousand board feet of lumber, six hundred feet of galvanized water pipe, and three months' supply of food.

"Great foolishness," said Keijo, surveying the assortment and critically picking up one of the bronze standard lamps. "What for you wanting this?"

"I don't know," I said, looking round apologetically. "It seems a pity to leave it behind."

Keijo's look made my spine crawl and I slunk behind a pile of lumber while he continued his inspection.

His snorts of disgust brought me out of hiding in time to see him deliver a hearty kick at a case of canned salmon.

"It is great foolishness to taking canned fish to a place where you can catching fresh fish," he roared.

"I know," agreed Jerry, on whom the curse of great foolishness was beginning to lose effect, "but we won't be doing any catching for a while. We have to build a house first. You said yourself that the cabin isn't fit for year-round living."

"It is still great foolishness," growled Keijo stubbornly as he climbed aboard the Monstrosity and disappeared into the engine-room.

In silence we continued with the loading while Keijo banged about in the bowels of the boat with a wrench.

"Surly bastard, isn't he?" said the head mover, walking across the deck to where we were standing. "I think we've got everything stowed away now. I've lashed those windows and doors down on top of the pilot-house, and the lumber is stacked on the after deck. Now, about that piano of yours——?"

I shook my head.

"No! No piano,' I said. "I'll store it. If things go wrong up there and we have to come back, we might have to live in it."

As I finished speaking, two or three small explosions followed by a loud and continuous clanking came from the engine-room. The whole boat shook like a jelly from stem to stern and everybody with the exception of Keijo leaped for the dock.

"My God! What happened?" exclaimed one of the men.

"Nothing," answered the wharfinger with an evil grin. "That's just a little sample of what happens when the engines get going."

Jerry released her breath in a gusty sigh.

"That settles it," she said firmly. "You and I are not going to travel on that thing—the furniture can take its chance, but *we* are going up on the steamer."

"How right you are, miss," said the moving-man, scratching his head and looking with pained surprise at the shaking freighter. "It sounds like a garbage can rolling downhill. I wouldn't send my mother-in-law out in a crate like that."

Keijo received our decision to travel on the steamer with his usual phlegmatic calm, and there being nothing to keep us in town, we left Keijo, who still had some unfinished business to complete, to follow at his leisure, and sailed away on the coast steamer one fine April morning, armed with a suitcase apiece, a week's supply of food, three spaniels, and a Pekinese.

The spaniels were a direct result of a magazine article which had described in glowing terms the lucrative returns to be obtained from the breeding of dogs. In this project, our capital investment had commenced wih one Pekinese and one small black animal, owned by Jerry, whose uncertain antecedents generally brought about the query: "What kind of a dog is that?" The answer, delivered in a tone of voice that admitted of no argument, was: "Her mother was a purebred spaniel." This was followed by a glare that effectively prevented any indiscreet inquiries regarding the father.

"You'll never raise anything worth while from her," I had said when Jerry, full of enthusiasm, had brought up the question of dog breeding.

"Sez who?" had demanded the insulted owner. "She's got good blood even if her father *was* a travelling man. If she had a purebred husband, she might have some nice pups."

Disregarding my doubtful looks, Jerry had paid a visit to some nearby kennels in search of the purebred husband, and a little later had come home in triumph towing a lemon-and-white cocker of the most irreproachable pedigree. During the introductions which followed, several small articles of furniture were overturned, and the prospective bride took two or three large bites out of her future husband, who retired into a corner howling dismally.

"She's shy," announced Jerry. "They say that true love often begins with a little aversion. We'll lock them up in the bathroom till they get to know one another."

The ensuing racket coming from the bathroom finally convinced us that the "little aversion" was rapidly turning into downright hate, and Jerry had picked up her coat and headed for the kennels again.

In due course she returned, leading still another cocker spaniel.

"Just as well to have a spare," she said in answer to my inquiring look. "The last one doesn't seem to have what it takes."

The new arrival was thrown in with the others, and the few days previous to our departure were made hideous by the lovesick yells of the bridal party rampaging about in the bathroom.

The Pekinese, a pampered pet of mine, possessed an ugly temper and an appetite out of all proportion to his size, and was known by the appropriate title of Chop Suey.

Keijo's face, when first confronted with this piece of Oriental degeneracy, had considerably shaken me.

"He making good fish bait," he had remarked with a nasty gleam in his eye.

"Why don't you leave the little beast in town?" said Jerry impatiently. "He won't be any use up there."

Faced with their combined opposition, I developed an unexpected streak of stubbornness.

"Why don't you leave some of those spaniels?" I had said crossly. "You know perfectly well we won't breed them. They don't do anything but fight."

"We might need them for hunting bears," said Jerry grimly. "Goodness only knows what we might run into where we are going."

"Why *three* of them?" I persisted.

"Some of them might get killed," answered Jerry calmly. "Nasty things, bears—especially grizzly bears."

A shiver of apprehension ran down my spine.

"Bears! Well, anyhow," I added, pulling myself together, "I'm taking Suey. He can help hunt bears too."

The day of our departure therefore found us with a string of hysterical spaniels and one highly irate Pekinese in addition to our other baggage, and the journey to the island was made to an accompaniment of long-drawn and homesick howls.

There were the usual stops for "boat landings" when an occasional small craft rocked out to pick up supplies and passengers, and there were the longer and more conventional delays at wharves belonging to logging communities, where in addition to the mountains of freight unloaded, lumbermen in their vivid-coloured clothing went ashore to work in the camps. At these latter places Jerry and I would collect the bride and suite and march them down the gangplank for exercise. As we walked them up and down on the wharf, we were painfully conscious of the critical looks and snide remarks directed at us by the natives lounging against the freight shed.

Jerry, striding by, hauling the three spaniels on a running lead, came off comparatively lightly in the barrage of criticism; but the appearance of Suey, bowlegged, goggle-eyed and panting at the end of his leash, always brought howls of mirth from the onlookers. The derisive comments concerning "queer-lookin' critters" and "fur-bearin' beetles" sent me, hot with embarrassment, racing up the gangplank long before the steamer's warning blast sounded.

"I told you not to bring him," said Jerry, looking at my flushed face.

"What else would you expect from a bunch of country bumpkins?" I replied. "How would they know anything about the royal dog of China? Most of them look as if they had been born in a hog-wallow."

It was evening before the steamer arrived in the vicinity of the island. The logging communities had long been left behind and the smell and noises of the city seemed part of another life. Our transportation from steamer to island had been taken care of, for Keijo had previously written a note to the strong-and-silent men advising them of our impending arrival and asking them to meet the boat.

With mounting excitement, we peered over the rail and saw the irregular outline of land through the blue dusk—the tall, pointed firs, the inlet with its towering snow-crested peaks, and the island in the foreground. The scent of spruce drifted to us across the water. The air was cold and clear and there was a sense of immense space and loneliness and above all, silence.

The engines slowed down. The siren blew a deep note which echoed among the mountains and a cluster of boats came dancing out of the gloom towards us. We descended to the freight deck of the steamer, where the mail sacks and freight were being unloaded onto different boats. The air was rank with the smell of stale vegetables rotting in their crates, and the roar of gasoline engines and the shouts of the different boatmen echoed in the still mountain air.

We threaded our way between piles of freight to the big opening in the side of the steamer, the dogs pulling at their leads and whining hysterically. Standing in the semi-darkness, we watched the boats crowding up beside us and the cartons and sacks of groceries being tossed into them. Occasionally a propeller or a spare part for a marine engine taxed the strength and agility of the crew as they endeavoured to drop it onto the deck of a rolling fishing boat.

A long, narrow dory with a sputtering inboard motor pulled up to the steamer and a burly figure in a mackinaw coat and wool cap called out:

"Have you got that copper pipe for Nels Olsen?"

"No—tell him it'll be up next week very likely."

The boatman dropped down into his dory, touched his engine and shot away into the gloom, and his place was taken by a battered row-boat occupied by an old man who received a sack of chicken feed and a roll of wire fencing.

"Coons still playing hob with your chickens, Lars?" asked the deck-hand as he handed down the roll of wire.

"Five of my best layers last night," cackled the old man in a high-pitched voice.

While we waited, the obliging deck-hands made inquiries for us as to which of the boats was going to Quiet Waters.

"Here you are, miss," said one of the men at last, as a fishing boat slid up beside us and lay rolling lazily, "this one's yours."

Through the window of the wheel-house, I caught a glimpse of the pilot's broad shoulders and golden hair.

"That isn't one of the strong-and-silent men," I whispered to Jerry. "Keijo said they were all dark."

"Hurry up if you're going ashore," said the deck-hand impatiently. "We're late already."

With some misgiving, we allowed ourselves to be helped into the fishing boat. The baggage was handed down to us, and the dogs, dangling from their collars like hanged criminals, were passed down to our waiting hands. Then to a chorus of rough shouts, ropes were cast off and our boat backed away. Again the siren echoed mournfully among the mountains as the engine-room bell rang. A foamy commotion started up around the steamer's propeller and she shuddered away into the night.

We looked about us unhappily. Our boat, heaving and tossing on the grey waves, was forging steadily ahead in company with various other small craft. In the pilot-house, the unbelievably handsome stranger stood gripping the wheel, his back turned towards us.

"Maybe we are being kidnapped," I whispered.

The thought was not unattractive.

"What are we doing on this man's boat? Ask him his name and see if he has a gun."

While I held down the rebellious dogs, Jerry ducked under the low door of the pilot-house and questioned the owner of the boat, who dissolved in an agony of blushes and gulped out explanations in halting English.

Presently she came out of the pilot-house shrugging her shoulders.

"I don't know who he is," she said. "I think he is a Norwegian. He said something about putting us ashore somewhere. I don't know how we got here in the first place and I don't think he does either. I didn't see any guns about and the man is so shy that he couldn't kidnap a mouse."

Resigned to whatever fate might have in store for us and wholly occupied with Suey, who was showing signs of imminent seasickness, we sat down on a heap of wet fishing nets in the back of the boat and watched the different craft gather together in the lee of a group of small rocky islets where the sorting of the mail took place.

One man, evidently acting as postmaster, turned the mail sacks upside down, sorted the meagre consignment into neat piles and slipped a rubber band round each one. Then, speaking with a strong Irish brogue, he called out the names of the waiting men and tossed each packet nonchalantly across the intervening waves to the rolling boats. When this haphazard mail delivery failed to reach its mark, the fishermen leaned over the side and hauled their packets out of the sea with dip-nets.

Mail distribution over, the boats drifted away one by one. The blond Norseman started his engine, took the wheel and without a word rolled away in the direction of land.

The roar of the rapids came to us above the splash of the waves and the thump of the motor. We sniffed the faint sweet scents of land appreciatively. The dogs pricked up their ears and their eager noses quivered; even Suey, puking vigorously and noisily over a can of stale fish bait, began to show signs of interest.

Accustomed to Keijo's reticence, we paid no attention to our silent guide but kept our eyes fixed on the shore-line; and presently we heard the motor stop as we drifted slowly up against the rocky cliffs that formed the ramparts of the island.

We were landed, complete with dogs and baggage, on a narrow shelf of rock outside the rapids, and the boatman gave us to understand that we were to wait there for slack tide and some rather problematical transportation in the shape of a row-boat brought out for us by one of the strong-and-silent men. Then without a backward glance the beautiful stranger headed his boat out to sea and disappeared from sight round a rocky promontory.

"Well, here we are," said Jerry, valiant but shaken. "Let's collect our stuff and sit down."

I looked round. The ledge was narrow, the cliffs behind steep, and just below us the sea heaved in an ominous manner. I tried to quell a rising tide of panic.

"Suppose no-one comes for us?" I whispered fearfully.

Jerry eyed me coldly.

"If no-one comes for us, I guess we shall just have to float through on our suitcases," she said.

We gathered our bags into a small heap, keeping a wary eye on the dogs who seemed to be making preparations to swim home again.

On the other side of the narrow gorge where the rapids raged in a milky froth, we could see the beautiful calm of Quiet Waters. In the soft half light the lagoon lay like a dark mirror filled with cloud reflections.

Behind it on the mainland, the mountain tops with their eternal snows shone white against the evening sky. Little by little, as the tide outside rose, the rushing of the rapids became less, and presently the upheaval subsided into an oily swirling, and out of the shadows came a small row-boat. Standing in the stern and paddling canoe fashion was a tall, heavy-set man dressed in hip boots and an oil-skin slicker. He was as dark as our previous guide had been fair, and to judge by the look of his features did not promise to be any more communicative. Greeting us with a flash of white teeth and a brief glance from deep-set eyes, he went about loading our baggage into his boat as if picking strange women off sea-lashed cliffs were an everyday occurrence.

"Can you speak English?" I asked hopefully when we were safely in his boat. A surprised look and a curt "Sure" was the only answer.

I sighed in relief.

"I guess you must be one of our neighbours then. I'm Margot, this is Jerry. What's *your* name?"

"'Lias."

"Oh."

After this brief interchange of remarks, conversation languished. The strong-and-silent man apparently had run out of small talk, and with his eyes fixed on a spot directly above our heads was pulling steadily at the oars.

I tried again.

"We rather expected you to meet us at the steamer."

"Yumph—boat engine busted."

"Oh, that's too bad. Did you ask the other man to come instead?"

"Yumph!"

"Who is he?"

"Christian."

I looked at Jerry in bewilderment.

"Aren't you all Christians here?"

A long silence.

"Nope—my name's 'Lias."

I blushed in embarrassment.

"I see, you mean his name is Christian?"

"Yumph!"

"What does he do?"

"Trap!"

"Where does he live?"

"Over there," with a sideways jerk of the head.

Exhausted by the strain of this conversation, I lapsed into silence and we glided between the smooth walls of the canyon and over the treacherous waters of the rapids, and began swinging up the lagoon to our new home.

The native habit of speechlessness began to envelop us too as the universal quiet began to penetrate our subconsciousness. My aimless chatter seemed out of place; relaxing, I listened dreamily to the sound of the oars dipping into the water.

Darkness had completely fallen before we reached the cabin. 'Lias ran the prow of his boat onto the beach. The frantic dogs leaped over the side and began running eagerly up and down, their noses glued to the earth.

With the help of 'Lias we dragged our belongings above high-water mark and then watched him row silently away.

With the sound of his oars fading in the distance, we stumbled blindly up the rocks, calling to the dogs who had scattered on strange scents, and arrived breathless at the cabin door.

"Let's leave the stuff down on the beach till morning," said Jerry. "All I want is a cup of tea and a good sleep."

We opened the door, struck a match and peering within, shuddered.

Between our hurried departure several months before and our present arrival things had deteriorated considerably.

The roof had been leaking. The mattresses and blankets which we had left behind us were damp and mildewed. The stove was red with rust. Famished-looking spiders leered at us from the cobwebs which festooned the roof, and among the mouse droppings on the table were the mouldy remains of our last meal, now covered with a thick coat of green fur.

"Cripes!" said Jerry in disheartened tones.

Hunting round in the dark, we found an end of candle stuck in a saucer and put a light to it.

"Did you say tea?" I wailed, looking round me. "We have to find wood to light the fire first."

"We have to fetch water from the lake, too," added Jerry.

I glanced through the open door into a blackness filled with

37

imaginary ghoulies and ghosties and long-legged beasties and echoing with things going bump in the night.

"Better take the dogs in case you meet any bears," I said, promptly disclaiming any responsibility for the fetching of water.

"Let's just go to bed and not bother with any tea," suggested Jerry.

"I think I'll sit up till daylight; I want to be sure there's nothing else in the bed but me."

In the end we compromised by shaking the blankets and splitting up an old apple box that had served as an extra seat, and while I lit a fire with the pieces, Jerry salvaged enough rusty-looking rain water from an old pail standing outside the door to make a pot of rather peculiar-tasting tea. A couple of cans of dog food providentially tucked into my overnight case saved the dogs from immediate starvation, and after we had seen them satisfied and strewn in attitudes of complete abandon round the stove, we lay down on the damp mattresses, and fully dressed, rolled ourselves in the damp blankets and settled down to sleep and digest our first taste of life lived "the hard way."

The fire in the stove slowly crackled out into a heap of grey ash. A gentle rain pattered on the roof, and thus began our adventure in paradise.

Chapter 3

THE HORRORS of the previous night were forgotten when we woke next morning to a day of brilliant sunshine. The sound of the sea and the rushing of the wind in the trees combined with the shouting of the seagulls on the beach below brought us tumbling out of our damp blankets in the wildest spirits.

Finding wood to light the fire and fetching water from the lake presented no problem in the daylight, and the nearest approach to a bear we saw was a small shy-eyed deer which slipped ghostlike out of the underbrush, looked at us hesitantly for a moment and then vanished as silently as it had appeared.

Breakfast was eaten to the fascinating sound of dry fir branches crackling in the stove and the scent of resin dripping into the ash box.

"There's something intoxicating about the scent of fried bacon out in the wilds," said Jerry. "In the city all you get is a room full of blue smoke and draperies smelling of stale fat, but out here—m'm, m'm!"

She sniffed the air ecstatically.

Once breakfast was over, we plunged into the business of restoring order in the littered cabin. Boxes and bags were hauled up from the beach, piles of dry wood gathered and stacked outside the door.

39

Several containers of fresh water were brought down from the lake. Blankets were laid out to air, and the cabin given a thorough scrubbing. The rusty stove was cleaned and polished, the dishes were washed and arranged on the shelves. The table in the window, where we ate our meals, was covered with a bright print cloth and a red pottery soup bowl filled with ferns and spruce tips was placed in the centre of it as a finishing decorative touch.

We found that the two boats which Keijo had agreed to sell "cheap" had been left bottoms-up on the beach. Looking at them closely, we found that neither boat would have been a bargain even as a gift. A good deal of repairing was necessary, to say nothing of a complete paint job. One boat was a ten-foot contraption almost square in shape and with a flat bottom. Owing to some peculiarity in construction, it had a tendency to ride in circles, and after one or two hilarious trial trips was unanimously christened *Dizzy Lizzy*.

Dizzy Lizzy, in spite of a disconcerting way of veering round in the opposite direction to that in which she was supposed to go, and an uncomfortable habit of slapping her flat bottom down on the waves, seemed to be reasonably seaworthy; but the other boat, on being launched, filled with water and sank.

"The timbers are probably dried out," said Jerry. "If we leave it to soak for a while, they may swell up."

The two boats were pushed out into shallow water and their long mooring ropes tied round large rocks on the beach. By afternoon the tide had risen and covered the rocks. The leaky boat had sunk to the level of her gunwales and *Dizzy Lizzy* was riding gaily about ten feet out from the shore.

We gazed at them in dismay.

"Looks like we'll have to swim out and dive for the ropes," said Jerry, kicking off her shoes and pulling her sweater over her head. Reluctantly I followed her example and after a suffocating session at the bottom of the sea, the mooring ropes were untied and the boats drawn up into shallow water and re-tied.

Several hours later the tide went out and left them high and dry on the rocks.

"We'll have to do something about this," I said as hands on hips I surveyed the bumps and scratches on the boats; but as neither of us had any ideas as to what to do, each change of tide saw us alternately swimming out after the boats or else tugging them off the rocks, and calling down loud curses on the sea and its restlessness.

Such minor irritants as this, however, were lost in the never ending miracle of being perfectly free to do exactly as we pleased.

We never seemed to get used to the fact that time did not mean anything. We could rise at any hour, knowing that there were no appointments to be kept and no buses to catch. The daily round, the common task was over, and we woke to a world as pure as the day on which it was created, and our nerves were no longer frayed by the clash of conflicting personalities.

The clock stopped, but it made no difference. We knew that daylight was the time for waking and dark the time for sleeping, and we ate when we were hungry. We began to forget what day it was, but that did not matter either because all days were alike.

For us, time had suddenly ceased to be.

Our lives were filled with fascinating new experiences from the early morning when we looked out at the moss-covered rocks, the wind-ruffled sea and the swaying forest, to the cool blue dusk of the evening with its silent stars and creeping shadows.

Each new sight and sound was an occasion for wonder and delight—the ever present seagulls, mewing plaintively overhead or waddling with contented quacks on the rocks; the red squirrels chattering at us from the branches of trees; a mink scurrying across the beach with a piece of dead fish; or an eagle soaring grandly in the sky above us.

Occasionally when following dim forest trails, we would come upon a cluster of deer feeding in a clearing and had time to notice their large eyes and the proud lift of their heads before they disappeared with graceful bounds into the forest.

Of bears or other marauding animals there was no sign.

While the dogs pounded feverishly up and down the hillside hot on the scent of jack-rabbits, we spent hours on the beach watching the dried-up barnacles come to life as the rising tide crept up. One by one as the waves lapped over them, each barnacle opened a tiny mouth, shot out a waving green feather of a tongue and began sweeping it vigorously back and forth in search of food. As the water crept higher, more and more barnacles opened until the rocks beneath the shallow margin were covered with a perfect forest of tiny waving green feathers.

We collected seaweed—bunches of rubbery sea flowers that embroidered the rocks like brown lace, long flat ribbons streaming in the fast-running tide, and rubber balls with long stems that went far down and attached themselves by tiny roots to the stones at the bottom of the sea.

On our first visit, Sundi had told us that she made pickles out of the upper part of the stem, and we looked wonderingly at the hard round things and speculated as to their taste.

In the rocky pools on the beach we discovered anemones of all colours, emerald, amethyst, pink and gold, opening like exotic flowers and shutting into tight shining buds at a touch. There were starfish clustering like jewels and silver jellyfish opening and shutting like tiny umbrellas in the crystal-clear water. In the woods behind the cabin, we found a humming-bird's nest, a tiny thing of moss and lichen laced to the underside of a cedar bough, and inside lay the unfledged humming-birds looking like four black bees. We looked and marvelled, and as we tiptoed away, a flash of iridescence shot past us with a thrum of invisible wings and hovered protectively over the nest. For the first time we saw a ruby-throated humming-bird in all its glittering plumage.

Occasionally we rowed down to the entrance to watch the boiling rapids which like a savage white monster guarded the lagoon. Once or twice we had arrived at the time of slack water, and the sight of the smooth evenly flowing tide had tempted us to float through towards the wide open sea outside, but fear of being unable to return kept us inside the lagoon.

"Some day," said Jerry, "when we have got used to the place and know when the tide changes, and how long it is between tides, we will go outside, but just at present we had better not take any chances." So we tied the boat to an overhanging tree at the water's edge, and rocking gently in the current, looked with curious eyes through the grim entrance at the big shining sea and the little islands dotting its surface.

Under our feet when we walked on the beach, clams spurted streams of water into the air, and hundreds of tiny black crabs slid with hard rustlings off the rocks into the sea.

"I never saw so much life," I said in wonder. "The place teems with it. I can't imagine why people should think the wilderness is lonely. It is much lonelier in the city. If you took all the people away there would be nothing but the deadness of man-made monuments, but here, where nobody lives, even the rocks seem to be alive."

In the evenings, we drifted on the water in *Dizzy Lizzy*, watching the shadows lengthen on the lagoon as the sun went down behind the black mountain ranges and the pale stars began to wink in the sky.

"How still it is!" murmured Jerry, resting on her oars and looking up at the sky. "I can feel peace spreading all over me like butter."

This idyllic state of affairs came to an abrupt halt when the end of the first week saw our supply of food practically exhausted and no sign of Keijo and the Monstrosity.

"I wonder what happened to him?" I said, looking sadly over our meagre food supply. "I thought he was to follow us up here the day after we left."

"Maybe he sank," commented Jerry gloomily.

"I wouldn't be surprised," I replied. "And where does that leave us?"

"Marooned," said Jerry nastily. "You always said you wanted to live on an island. You've got your wish—now what are you going to do about it?"

Once again neither of us had any ideas as to how to handle the situation, and gradually our stock of provisions diminished to the point where we were reduced to meals of dry bread and black coffee.

We began to cast speculative eyes in the direction of our homesteading neighbours.

Since our arrival we had seen no sign of the strong-and-silent men, and in the absence of any friendly overtures from them, pride forbade our seeking help in that quarter. Sundi had gone with her husband and left the farm in charge of the Danish hired man, who for all we had seen of him could have been completely non-existent.

Ravenous with hunger and spurred on by memories of tasty homespun meals served to us when visiting Keijo's farm, we decided that the time had come to dispense with formalities.

"It's no use standing on ceremony when you are starving to death," said Jerry. "I'm going to find this Danish character and see if I can buy some food."

Without further discussion we marched down to the beach, ripe for action.

The tide was full and the boats were floating a long way out. I looked at them in disgust.

"Pity you can't train them to come when you whistle."

A certain amount of time was lost before *Dizzy Lizzy*'s mooring line was retrieved. The rock to which it was fastened was heavy and it took a lot of diving, tugging and coming up for air before the knot was loosened; but once the boat was freed, we lost no time in rowing up the lagoon, tying the boat to the wharf and walking boldly up to the house.

I tapped at the door. Nothing happened. I tapped again.

"Maybe he's out," I suggested.

"He isn't—there's smoke coming out of the chimney," said Jerry.

After several more tappings, each more vigorous than the last, we heard a faint sound. The door opened a crack and an eye appeared in the opening.

"Good morning," I said uncertainly. "We are your new neighbours."

The eye continued to glare through the crack, and I looked at Jerry for help.

"We have run out of provisions and we wondered if we could buy some from you until Keijo brings our supplies up from town," said Jerry, stepping valiantly into the breach.

44

The door opened slowly, and we came face to face with Holge, the Danish hired man.

This was the first time we had seen him and after the giant specimens of island residents we had already encountered, Holge came as a distinct shock.

He was a dark, wizened little man with stooped shoulders and a frightened face that puckered up into a network of wrinkles when speaking, and his voice was so soft that it was almost inaudible.

Having satisfied himself that we were harmless, he welcomed us in fluent but impossibly mispronounced English, and on our again explaining the purpose of our visit, informed us sadly that he was also anxiously awaiting the arrival of Keijo with supplies, and was not in much better plight than ourselves, Keijo having taken the precaution before he left of locking up the stores of canned fruit, vegetables, game and fish.

In execrable English Holge told us that there was no hay for the cows, no feed for the chickens, "—even for me d'ere iss no feed," he finished mournfully.

We looked at him—stunned.

"You mean to say that on a farm there is nothing to eat?" said Jerry. "I don't believe it."

We looked about us.

The new spring vegetables were barely showing above the ground. The feed for the livestock was rationed down to the last straw, and investigation proved only too well the truth of Holge's assertion that the large storehouse full of provisions was securely padlocked.

"He iss a hardt man," sighed Holge looking at us with sad dark eyes, and his narrow shoulders sagged as he gave us to understand that all he had to offer was milk, eggs, some very old potatoes, and clams—the latter article being in his estimation food unfit for Christian consumption.

"Why don't you kill a cow or a chicken?" asked Jerry incredulously. "They are going to die anyway if there is no food for them. We'll pay Keijo for them when he comes back—if he ever does."

45

Holge looked at her with horror and the wrinkles on his face chased each other like waves across his worried countenance as he explained that he was held personally responsible for every hair and every feather on the place, and the killing of a chicken, even a half-dead one, would be regarded by Keijo as a crime so heinous that his reason faltered at the thought of the consequences.

"Oh, never mind!" said Jerry impatiently. "We'll buy some eggs and milk then."

Shyly, Holge told us that he had been preparing his dinner when we had arrived and would be pleased to share it with us, and on our accepting his invitation led us into the house and seated us at the table while he set before us a combination of foods which he described as "clem zoop" and "potched ekks."

Overcome by the excitement of unaccustomed visitors, Holge skittered about the kitchen, spilling soup, clattering dishes and banging jugs of milk down on the table while Jerry and I, ravenous from our compulsory dieting, ate with relish everything in sight.

When we had finished, we returned to the beach full of food and heartfelt thanks, followed by Holge chattering unintelligibly and carrying two cans of milk and a box of eggs.

For the next few days we lived on a diet of milk and eggs, served to a steady stream of complaints from Jerry concerning "invalid slop."

"What I wouldn't give for a juicy beef-steak!" she said gloatingly. "Every time I see Keijo's cows I feel like going up and taking a bite out of them."

We rationed out the remaining dog food into small portions. The spaniels looked at us as only a spaniel knows how to look and Suey was vociferous in his disapproval of the new system of dieting. His grunts of disgust over his curtailed dinner proclaimed the fact that he had always known that no good would ever come of this mad adventure.

Urged on by a need for something else to eat besides eggs and milk, Jerry took to haunting the woods, with an improvised slingshot and a pocket full of stones, while I investigated the clam beds down by the rapids and dug up a bucket full of small butter clams.

"How do we get them out of the shell?" I asked, watching Jerry turning them over in a vain endeavour to find a crack in their armour into which a knife could be inserted. "I never saw a clam on the hoof before; somehow I had an idea that they always grew in cans."

In our abysmal ignorance we tried breaking them with rocks, and reduced the contents of the shells to pulp in the process.

Remembering Holge's "clem zoop," we sought him out and asked for information on the art of shelling clams. Under his directions we learnt how to soak the clams in a bucket of fresh water until the sand had drained away, after which the water was poured off and the clams placed on the stove to steam themselves open.

Two days' meals consisting entirely of clams found us completely surfeited and fully in accordance with Holge's conviction that clams were fit only for a heathen. We returned to our former meals of milk and eggs—eggs boiled, fried, poached and scrambled, until Jerry in despair declared that our native speech was beginning to degenerate into clucks.

We saw a good deal of Holge at this time. Having overcome his initial shyness, he clung to us with a sort of desperation and never a day passed without his rowing over to see if by some miracle of second sight we could tell him what had happened to Keijo; and sitting on the rocks by the sea, we exchanged possible reasons for his continued absence.

As we came to know him better, Holge began to reveal secret aspirations that filled us with amazement. Beneath his frightened exterior he harboured a great ambition to become a dictator and lead a nation. He combined an abject fear of the domineering Keijo with an ardent admiration for such men as Napoleon and Hitler, and insisted that Stalin was the greatest man that had ever lived. It all stemmed, no doubt, from a natural reaction against his own feebleness of body and purpose.

On our trips across to collect eggs and milk, we used frequently to find him lying under the apple trees poring intently over books dealing with the art of dictating. The theories of Karl Marx he could recite by heart. He also possessed a dog-eared copy of *Mein Kampf*, which he read in the original. The different ideologies seemed to mean nothing to him, and the main purpose of his reading was apparently to try and discover the secret magic that created a dictator.

His ludicrous habit of raising his right arm when emphasizing his arguments, accompanied by much stamping of feet and clicking of heels, reduced us to helpless giggles and left us wondering which particular form of dictatorship he was following at the moment.

His favourite form of greeting was a gesture which combined the "Heil Hitler" salute with the clenched fist of the Communists, and the sight of the stoop-shouldered little figure coming up the beach with upraised arm generally brought ironic answering gestures from us. During our conversations with him, we had discovered that Holge had been the runt in a family of large men. Unable to hold his end up among his giant brothers, he had endeavoured to bolster his bruised ego with fantastic dreams of some day dominating a nation.

His emigration to America had followed the reading of an over-heated pamphlet which led him to believe that all the people on the American continent lived like kings, ate like kings, were housed in luxurious mansions, drove large and glittery cars, and collected fabulous wages for doing practically nothing. For a time visions of returning to Denmark in style with one of the large, glittery cars and carelessly tossing mounds of good American dollars about to the envy of his less fortunate relatives had superseded his dreams of dictatorship; but things had not worked out that way. Holge had drifted aimlessly, frightened, lonely and often out of work, and his bright dreams had ended, according to him, in his being "left on an island without food."

Working long hours for a pittance he accepted as in the natural order of things, but being left on an island without food was another matter, and his lamentations over this fate were long and continuous.

"We can't do anything about being left on an island," I said one day, "but surely we can do something about food. There are lots of fish in the sea. Haven't you got a fishing-line?"

No, Holge had not got a fishing-line. Fishing was Keijo's business, not his. Besides, all the fishing tackle was locked up in the storehouse.

I remembered seeing a gun rack in Keijo's kitchen.

"How about you shooting a deer?"

Holge's wrinkles worked violently as he looked at me with terror-filled eyes and confessed that he had never fired a gun in his life, and the sight of blood turned him sick.

Watching him as he crept away with sagging shoulders, I laughed a little scornfully.

"There goes a fine threat to the world."

Jerry looked after him with a thoughtful frown.

"I don't know—it's just these people who have been pushed around all their lives that *are* a threat to the world. Given half a chance, they start doing the pushing themselves. Properly handled, I think Holge could become a real menace."

If Holge proved to be a broken reed when it came to the providing of food, he made up for it by his knowledge of boats. Coming across us one day when we were diving for *Dizzy Lizzy's* mooring-line, he timidly suggested that if we would allow him, he might be able to arrange an easier way of anchoring the boats.

Overjoyed, we watched while he went to work on a system of lines and pulleys which allowed the boats to ride out in deep water when not in use, and made it possible to pull them in to shore when needed. He also repaired the leaky boat with a mixture of pitch and resin, and carved us an extra pair of light oars out of cedar.

"That's wonderful, Holge," I said gratefully. "Thanks so much. I would never have thought of anything like that. You are a real help to us."

Holge expanded under the praise and his eyes fastened on us with an expression of almost doglike devotion.

"I honestly think that this is the first time in his life anyone has ever said a kind word to him," said Jerry, watching him trotting happily down to his boat.

Next morning his temporarily inflated ego collapsed and we saw him hurrying up the trail with his wrinkled face a mask of despair.

I met him at the door.

"Heil Hitler!" I said solemnly, raising my right arm.

For once there was no response. Holge tripped over the doorstep and practically fell into the cabin, gasping: "Katie's in de slough! Katie's in de slough!"

"Katie?" queried Jerry.

"Yess—in de slough! In de slough!"

I looked at Jerry and chuckled inwardly.

"Who would have thought it of Holge?" I murmured. "I wonder where he's been hiding her all this time?"

Holge sank limply onto one of the cots.

"She can't get up. She iss weak from starvation," he went on, wiping his pallid face with a dirty handkerchief with red and white spots.

"I'll bet!" said Jerry fervently.

"I left her in de meadow so dat she eat de grass," moaned Holge.

To me, this seemed to be carrying starvation to extremes, and I looked at Jerry in bewilderment.

"Dis morning she wass in de slough. I t'ink her hind leg broke."

"*Hind* leg?" said I, a horrid suspicion crowding out the mental picture I had formed of beauty in distress. "Just a minute—who *is* this Katie?"

"De cow, de Holstein cow."

Thoroughly deflated, we sank down in our chairs.

"What do I do?' asked Holge, looking at us pathetically.

"Lift her out," I suggested helpfully.

"Shoot her," said Jerry, her mind obviously running on the possibility of fresh beef-steak.

Holge looked at us miserably and wrung his hands. Overcome by the magnitude of the disaster and the prospect of Keijo's wrath, the would-be dictator had become an inept little being shivering with fright and quite unable to cope with the situation.

"We'll come over later when we have had lunch," Jerry assured him, and he went away disconsolate while we turned to the ever present problem of finding a new way to cook an egg.

Later on, our investigations at the scene of the accident revealed a scrawny black and white cow lolling contentedly in the mud while a pale and anxious Holge hovered over her offering handfuls of parched grass, covering her with the blankets from his bed, and looking less than ever like the popular conception of a dictator.

Jerry and I walked about the disaster area trying to think up ways and means of pulling Katie out of her mud bath.

With Holge's anxious and imploring eyes fixed on me, I tried to rise to the heights of knowledge obviously expected.

"How about a block and tackle?" I suggested tentatively, having in my mind a confused impression of a tangle of ropes fastened to something or other and with a man tugging at one end and a heavy weight being raised at the other. Holge required more detailed information, and being unable to provide it, I hurriedly changed ground.

"Have you tried digging her out?"

Holge shook his head despairingly and indicated that the mud was so soft that any attempt to dig might cause Katie to sink even deeper.

Some experimental shoving, in which Holge and Jerry joined forces, ended in their both joining Katie in the slough.

"Oh, come on home," said Jerry impatiently, shaking the mud from her shoes. "I don't know why he bothers about the ugly old brute. She just enjoys being fussed over. I bet she would get out quick enough if he left her alone."

"Look, Holge," I said, impressed by the terror in his eyes, "try and get someone else to help you. We can't do anything."

Holge, thrown on his own resources, decided to enlist the aid of the strong-and-silent men, and we watched with interest for the arrival of this new element.

"We'll see if *they* have anything to eat besides eggs," said Jerry, licking her lips in anticipation.

Our eager hopes were doomed to disappointment, however, for

the men arrived unobtrusively at a time when Jerry and I were hovering over a rock pool with a piece of string, optimistically trying to entice a flatfish into swallowing a bent pin baited with hard-boiled egg. After restoring Katie to a more normal position, they had left as quickly and as quietly as they had come.

"Why didn't they come to see us?" exclaimed Jerry indignantly when informed of the visit.

"They are very shy," explained Holge, his anxious face creased like a wet sheet.

"Well," I said grimly, "when we have died of starvation I hope they won't be too shy to come and bury us."

Next day was mail day. The good-natured Holge took on himself the task of rowing out to the steamer to pick up our mail and to find out from the crew if they had heard any news of the missing Keijo.

Towards evening I divided the last can of dog food between the anxious-faced dogs, while Jerry watched me and gloomily reviewed our own recent meal at which I had served up my latest culinary invention—a dish of scrambled potatoes and eggs moistened with tomato catsup and the juice from an empty pickle jar. Judged by any standards it could not have been called a success, and our opinions concerning "islands without food" were rapidly beginning to match those of Holge.

Dusk fell over the lagoon and along with it came Holge, rowing furiously, splashing up the water with his oars, shouting incoherently and casting frequent looks over his shoulder in our direction. Babbling insanely, he ran the prow of his boat up on the beach and scrambled out, scattering our letters and parcels all over the place in his nervous haste.

"Stop screeching, Holge," said Jerry impatiently. "Say what you have to say slowly so that we can understand you."

Holge subsided and his eyes lost their wild look as he relapsed into his normal state of timidity; and we gradually got at the substance of his ravings, which was that the Monstrosity had been sighted chunking steadily along lower down the coast-line and would in all probability arrive at the lagoon next morning.

"Thank God!" said Jerry with a pious glance upward. "One more egg and I'll begin to sprout feathers."

In Holge, however, the news of Keijo's imminent arrival raised up a host of fears: a vegetable garden, the hoeing of which had been neglected while he had studied the art of dictatorship; an axe handle which he had broken and which Keijo's eagle eye would be sure to notice; and last and most important of all, the fact that he had allowed Katie to tumble in the slough. This last episode seemed to cause him so much apprehension that we were amazed.

"Don't tell him," I said bluntly. "He'll never guess."

Holge shook his head, his eyes glazed with fright, and explained that the incriminating evidence was there in the mud on Katie's flanks and the slight limp which still remained as an aftermath of the accident.

"It wasn't your fault," said Jerry in an attempt at consolation. "Tell him so. We'll back you up."

But Holge was beyond consolation and we watched him leave, his narrow shoulders sagging more than ever and his sad eyes staring hopelessly ahead.

Next morning we were up with the birds and over at Keijo's wharf impatiently waiting for the arrival of the Monstrosity.

"Slack tide is around nine o'clock," said Jerry, consulting Holge's tide book. "It's a full one, too. Keijo should be able to run the rapids easily, and then—oh boy! What a meal I'm going to have."

"Cheer up, Holge," I said, looking at the Dane's dismal face. "He won't beat you. We won't let him."

But Holge was more concerned over the possible loss of his job, thankless and ill-paid as it was.

"Vere vill I get anudder?" he said in despair. "Nobody effer vants me."

"Don't worry. Keijo won't fire you," said Jerry unkindly. "He'll never get anyone else to work for the wages he pays you."

Holge looked suddenly hopeful.

"Maybe I take less, den he keep me on."

53

"Don't be silly. Stick up for your rights. If you take less now, the first thing you know you'll be working for nothing."

"I would still haff food and a bed," murmured the poor Dane faintly.

We looked at him with pity and impatience but further attempts at consolation were interrupted by the distant and welcome sound of a garbage can rolling downhill; and a few minutes later the Monstrosity, shivering and rattling, bumped up against the wharf and Keijo's cold and rigid face looked down on us from the pilot-house.

Leaving Sundi and Holge to fasten the mooring-ropes, Jerry and I swarmed up her sides and, rudely disregarding Sundi's attempted explanation of the engine troubles which had delayed them, dived down into the hold. Charging into the cases of provisions, we broke open a crate of oranges.

A little later when we emerged, breathless and smeary, from underneath a mound of orange peel, we became aware of sounds of strife coming from the direction of the orchard, where Keijo was bullying the defenceless and unhappy Dane. No time had evidently been lost in discovering the broken axe handle and the unhoed vegetable garden, and now Keijo was busy extracting every last detail concerning the story of Katie and the slough.

"Come on," said Jerry after a few moments of horrified listening. I followed her as she stumbled out of the hold, leapt from the deck to the wharf and raced across the beach to the orchard where the battle was raging. Here we found that any effort to help Holge was quite futile when Keijo suddenly decided that he did not understand English.

Looking at us with a cold and apparently uncomprehending eye, he swept us aside with an insulting gesture and reverting to his own language continued his abuse of the now thoroughly demoralized hired man.

"Don't pretend you don't understand English," I shouted in a rage; then, descending to lower levels, I added, "—you blasted old Finn!"

Keijo stopped his tirade and looked at me coldly.

"Yes, I *am* a Finn," he stated, but evidently disclaimed the qualifying adjective.

Jerry seized me by the arm and drew me away.

"Let's go and talk to Sundi," she whispered.

Our championship of Holge drew no response from that quarter either. Sundi was completely under the thumb of her husband and *he* said that Holge was a villain, so Holge undoubtedly was a villain, and all our pleadings fell on deaf ears. Sundi merely looked at us with round blue eyes and shook her blond head.

"*He* say—"

"Oh, to hell with him!" I interrupted rudely and flung out of the house.

We returned to the ship and commenced loading cases of provisions into our row-boats.

"I feel we have let Holge down somehow," I said, "but what can you do with a man who won't speak English unless it suits him and a woman whose mind is still in the Dark Ages?"

"I'll talk to Keijo tomorrow when he has cooled down," said Jerry, "and you stay home. You only make matters worse by losing your temper."

We rowed away, our boats boiling over with cartons of assorted groceries. In one boat a sack of potatoes and a sack of onions leaned companionably together on the rear seat. In the other, a side of bacon and a cheese rode side-saddle on top of a box of apples, while over the sides and under the seats, canned meats, vegetables, chicken and fish sprawled in a riot of confusion. Over the water, the sound of angry voices followed us until we were out of earshot and floating into the peace of our own little bay, where we saw the four dogs, ears acock, sitting in a row hopefully waiting for us.

"Look what we've got for you!" called Jerry, leaping exuberantly out onto the shale. "For once you shall have all the food you can eat."

With the dogs jumping about us, we tugged the cartons uphill to the cabin, unpacked them and distributed cans of horsemeat to the hungry animals, after which we lit the fire, clapped on the kettle, and plunged into an orgy of eating with no holds barred.

A long time after, we lay replete on the mossy rocks outside the cabin listening to the faint sounds drifting to us on the still air from the direction of Keijo's homestead. Once we saw Holge row desperately away into the centre of the lagoon with Keijo in hot pursuit in another boat. A violent argument seemed to be still in progress, and boats rocked wildly and arms flailed in forceful gestures as the two men disputed; then we saw Holge pick up his oars again and head for the shore, Keijo following him with grim determination. After this we heard no more, and the rest of the day we spent in restocking our empty larder shelves and our equally empty interiors.

When night fell we retired to our narrow cots in a state of satiation. The following morning Jerry rowed over to Keijo's homestead, determined to make a final effort to intercede in Holge's behalf. In a little while she returned with a glum face. Neither Keijo nor Holge was to be found. Sundi was not helpful, all Jerry's inquiries as to their whereabouts being met with a blank blue stare and a slow head-shake.

"What a household!" exclaimed Jerry in disgust. "It makes you wonder if women in Finland have voting privileges. Somebody should tell her."

Another day passed while we worried and fretted about Holge, and our imaginations outrivalled all the plots of all the murder mysteries we had ever read.

"I bet Keijo has cut Holge's throat with the broken axe and buried him in the vegetable garden to make up for the hoeing he didn't do—a sort of making the punishment fit the crime, you know," I suggested.

Our fears for Holge's life were quite unjustified. Next morning, with the sun shining brilliantly and happy memories of a breakfast of the best smoked ham still with us, we were busily sweeping out the cabin when Holge appeared in the doorway garbed in an overcoat of Napoleonic cut and an old felt hat which somehow he had managed to invest with a military air, and announced that he had come to say good-bye.

"Oh Holge, I'm so glad you are all right!" I said thankfully. "We tried to talk to Keijo but one might just as well talk to a brick wall."

"We were afraid Keijo might have murdered you," said Jerry, standing at the window and reflectively eating canned plums which she picked dripping out of their container.

Holge's beaten eyes stared hopelessly out of his lined face and in faltering English he gave an account of two days living under a constant stream of cruel invective by the unforgiving Keijo, at the end of which time he had received his dismissal almost with relief.

"And so you are really leaving us?" I said with genuine regret.

"I shall miss you," said Jerry, adding in an attempt to be flippant, "every time I eat an egg I'll think of you."

Holge's tired eyes brightened and his wrinkled face relaxed.

"Dat vill be nice," he said simply. "Nobody hass effer missed me."

"What will you do now, Holge?" I asked.

"I go home to Denmark."

"Have you enough money?" I asked tentatively, thinking of Keijo's meagre wages.

For a moment a tiny gleam of pride showed in Holge's eyes.

"I vork my passage back. Dat is de vay I kom—dat is de vay I go."

He shook hands solemnly, clicked his heels, raised his right arm in a last dramatic gesture of farewell, and left. Presently we saw Keijo grimly rowing him out to meet the steamer as he started on his long journey home.

We waved enthusiastically from the shore and I felt a little pang as I saw him go. In the short time we had been together, we had unconsciously grown fond of the timid little man with the big ideas.

"He deserves better of life," I said, thinking that there are other forms of murder than the purely physical. "He is one of those people who are bound to be losers, whichever side they are on."

For the next day or two we went about our business thoughtfully and carefully avoided Keijo's homestead, and presently Sundi came over with a jug of fresh cream and an invitation to come and look at a crop of freshly hatched chickens.

Her jolly laugh was the same as always and no mention was made of the unfortunate Holge. On our meeting Keijo coming out of the cow barn, our wary greetings were received with the usual unintelligible grunt and the contemptuous expression he reserved for that low form of life—woman.

By degrees life returned to normal. The sun shone. We had plenty of food and we were happy. The pitiful figure of Holge gradually faded from our minds. Keijo unbent occasionally and condescended to speak to us on the occasions when he brought in our mail from the steamer, and we learnt our first lesson—that beautiful surroundings do not necessarily make beautiful characters.

Chapter 4

WHEN WE had first discussed our pioneering plans with our horrified friends, the only person who had not joined in the general chorus of condemnation had been my youngest brother, Alan.

Instead of the storm of protest which we had come to expect, he had greeted the idea with whoops of joy, listened to our plans enviously and vowed that he would follow us up to our island as soon as possible to give us a hand in raising the new home.

While waiting his arrival, Jerry and I decided to get into training for this event by felling some of the young firs that grew in clusters on the proposed site of the house.

After some tremendous axe swinging that produced no results other than an axe blade with a permanent wave in it and a tree trunk that looked as if it had been chewed by rats, we abandoned the axes and took to sawing.

As far as we were concerned, the term "undercut" was a word confined solely to sirloin roasts, and any idea of applying it to a tree-felling operation had never entered our heads. Our main method of procedure was to saw patiently until the saw blade jammed, then attack the tree from another angle with a new saw and keep alternately working at them until they met in the middle. When the tree showed signs of moving, we downed tools and ran for our lives.

This nonchalant and unorthodox method had the effect of reducing Keijo's English vocabulary to shreds, but it produced results of a sort, as we pointed out to our grim, unsmiling neighbour.

Undaunted by his frigid disapproval, we worked away until a letter from Alan announcing his imminent arrival accompanied by two crates of Leghorn hens set us off on another tack.

"*Hens!*" exclaimed Jerry blankly. "Oh my hat, the hens! I'd forgotten all about them. Where on earth are we going to put them?"

"We need a chicken house," I said, "and we need it quick. Come on, never mind these trees, let's start building."

The tree felling was forgotten as we set to work on this new project.

"Let's see, the front elevation should face the sea," I said, vague recollections of architectural blueprints floating through my mind. "After all, even a chicken likes to have a view."

It took us several days to locate the site for this desirable residence. One place we considered too far from the house, another too close to the house, still another we decided looked like a possible camping spot for bears, and on a fourth we found raccoon tracks.

"No use looking for trouble," said Jerry, poring over the marks. "Coons and chickens just don't mix well."

When we were both finally agreed on the place, we set about clearing it.

The saws and axes were once more brought into play, only this time we ran into real trouble. There were one or two age-old fir trees which had to be removed before the building of the chicken house could be commenced, and on the first one we used up all our saws and broke the hafts of two of our axes.

"Something wrong somewhere," said Jerry in puzzled tones as we sat on our haunches looking at the great tree, bristling on all sides with saws that had jammed.

"Maybe Keijo could tell us what to do," I suggested. "There must be an easier way than this."

On the pretext of buying some of Katie's milk, we rowed across to the farm and casually stated our problem.

Keijo looked at us with ice-blue eyes cold and uncomprehending, then he looked from us to his wife questioningly. A torrent of Finnish passed between them while we stood uncomfortably by, and it ended in Keijo's picking up his leather jacket and accompanying us back to the scene of operations.

One look at the tree trunk stuck through with saws that had jammed had the effect of shaking him out of his natural stolidity, and he looked from the tree to us with incredulous horror.

"You no cutting tree down so. You must using wedges," he declared.

"Wedges?" echoed Jerry, an inquiring upswing to her voice. "You mean those iron things that are thick at one end and thin at the other?"

Comprehension began to dawn on me.

"So *that's* what they are for," I said, as under Keijo's tutelage we learnt how to hammer the wedges into the saw cut in such a way that the weight of the tree was thrown forward and the saw enabled to move backwards and forwards easily.

"It's so easy when you know how," I said after Keijo had gone and the tree in all its stricken magnificence was lying on the ground.

Jerry rose from her knees where she had been counting the rings on the stump.

"Eighty-two," she said with a sigh. "What a long time it takes to grow and what a short time to die."

We looked at the other forest giants stretching their green arms skyward and soberly decided to build the chicken house somewhere else.

The next site chosen was deficient in trees, but had an over-abundance of rocks. We tugged them to one side and piled them. Once the patch of ground was cleared and levelled, we fenced it. The idea of using our rolls of second-hand hog fencing as a means of keeping chickens within bounds was thoroughly scouted by Keijo; so, in the absence of chicken wire, we improvised a fence of slender vertical poles, hundreds of them, nailed close together on cross-pieces and set up in sections. The finished production resembled something the early pioneers might have built to protect themselves from Indians.

Keijo's acid comments left us unmoved, and we used to stand, head aside, and view this masterpiece with intense satisfaction. For the first time in our lives we experienced the thrill that comes from doing a thing yourself, no matter how badly it is done. The most appallingly amateurish affair became a thing of wondrous beauty when it was the work of our own scratched and aching hands.

A supply of two-by-fours and shiplap had come up on the Monstrosity with our furniture. Some of this we decided to use to build the chicken house, and a long happy day was spent hauling it out of the hold, throwing it overboard, and towing it piecemeal round to our bay, where we beached it and carried it up the hill, one board at a time. This done, we assembled our tools and set to work.

Keijo's scorn was no match for his curiosity and we noticed that he had begun to have some mysterious business in the forest that bordered our land, a business that entailed his crossing over almost every day near the spot where we were working. Mostly he passed us in silence, apparently looking straight ahead, but actually never missing a thing. It was rarely that he spoke.

"You no can building house," he said in contemptuous tones when we ventured to ask him for information regarding foundations. "It falling down."

"Like hell it will," retorted Jerry, stung beyond endurance by his constant and adverse criticism. "We've got as much intelligence as most people. I *know* we can do it."

"You not even having spirit level," sneered Keijo, surveying our collection of tools with scorn.

"What's that?" I inquired innocently.

A well-directed kick on the shins by Jerry prevented me from displaying any more of my ignorance, and we retired with dignity into the cabin to search The Book for information on building.

The Book had nothing to say regarding the building of chicken houses by beginners, but offered an advanced course in cucumber frames and septic tanks.

"We'll just have to use our common sense," said Jerry, shutting up the volume and getting up from her chair. "Let's take a look at the underneath part of the cabin and see how it is put together."

A careful and detailed inspection of the cabin's foundations revealed the fact that it was built on logs laid across flat rocks.

"Nothing to it," said Jerry briskly. "We'll cut down some trees, and there are all kinds of rocks lying around."

During the laying of the foundations, the need for a spirit level became glaringly apparent, "—unless we want the chickens all toboganning downhill," said Jerry, surveying the angle of the floor. "I wonder what people did before spirit levels were invented?"

I took a tentative step across the sloping floor.

"They must have had remarkably straight eyesight, or else they all had one leg shorter than the other," I answered, limping back to level ground. "How about using a glass of water?"

A drinking-glass circled with red and black rings, filled with water, made an admirable substitute for a spirit level. The floor was laid and we proceeded with the erection of the walls.

By following the plan of the cabin carefully, we managed to raise the framework of two-by-fours and cover it with shiplap without too much trouble, and it was not until we got to the roof that we had to confess ourselves beaten. Attempts to follow the peaked-roof plan of the cabin resulted in complete failure; and the frequent collapse of pairs of two-by-fours precariously balanced end to end threatened to bring about the ruin of the whole shaky structure.

"Oh damn—it's worse than building a house of cards," said Jerry, rubbing an ankle which had got in the way of a crashing timber. "Let's forget the roof. They won't be needing one this weather, and in the winter we can use a tarpaulin."

This easy and cowardly solution of the roofing problem brought the end of the building in sight. We constructed some perches, nesting boxes and feed troughs. We made a little door for the chickens to come out, and a big door for us to go in, after which we spent a whole afternoon admiring it from every possible angle. We rowed across to Keijo's farm and invited him to come and see it; but Keijo, without a smile on his granite face, coldly said that he did not need to see it. He could imagine it.

A few days later, Alan arrived in a cloud of poultry and profanity. Having at the last minute decided to burden himself with half a dozen patent drinking fountains and some quite unnecessary egg-candling equipment, he had by-passed the steamer and chartered a fishing boat to bring himself and impedimenta up to the island. After an hour's hovering about outside the rapids, eyeing the churning white water with suspicious eyes, the owner of the boat, urged on by the impatient passenger, had decided to take a chance and force a passage through. The boat, swirling in the current, struck a submerged rock, and it was a scared and thoroughly disgruntled pair of men who piloted the badly listing boat into the lagoon.

"Of all the cockeyed places to get into!" growled Alan, when we had rowed out to meet him. "Someone ought to blast that channel out. It isn't safe."

"It's safe enough if you wait for slack tide," I told him. "Besides we like it this way. Think of the privacy it gives us."

Alan looked back over his shoulder with loathing, and uttering disapproving grunts, proceeded to unload the chicken crates onto our row-boats. The fishing boat was eased up onto Keijo's ways for repairs, and Jerry and I gleefully landed the crates and released the chickens, which we promptly housed in the new structure, and which as promptly flew out of it.

"What do you expect, with no roof on the damn thing?" asked Alan as, hands on hips, he looked disparagingly at the result of our labours. "I'd better get a roof on tomorrow or you won't have any hens left. . . . Call off those dogs while I unpack my stuff."

The next few days were busy ones. Driven by a young brother bursting with energy, we stood patiently by handing him tools, lumber and nails while he covered the chicken house with something which he described as a "shed" roof, an affair considerably less complicated than the peaked roof which we, in our ignorance, had attempted to construct.

The chickens safely under cover, we left them to a process described by Jerry as producing "an egg per chicken per day perhaps," and turned to unloading the furniture and the rest of the lumber off the Monstrosity. This took us several days. Each article had to be hauled by hand out of the hold to the deck and then with infinite difficulty lowered over the side of the boat onto a large raft grudgingly lent by Keijo. There were heavy pieces of furniture, hundred-pound crates of books, long sections of water pipe, sacks of chicken feed and of peat moss, and piles of dressed lumber.

Keijo kept strictly apart. Standing on the shore, he watched our struggles with a coldly critical eye, occasionally muttering comments on the unnecessary amount of equipment we had thought important for a life lived "the hard way."

"There's no need for us to be uncomfortable," I told him impatiently. "We might just as well sit on a soft chair as a hard one."

"You no needing soft chairs," replied Keijo stolidly, " you no needing chairs at all. I always living the hard way. The hard way best."

Apparently his philosophy of life did not include trying to smooth the hard way for others, because not once did he offer to help us, although sometimes the hauling of the big crates out of the hold taxed our combined strength to the utmost.

"I suppose if we asked him to help, he would," I said after three attempts to pull the chesterfield out of the hold had ended in failure.

"I wouldn't ask that miserable swine for a crust if I was starving," replied Alan wrathfully. "Give me a chance to get my breath and we'll have another go at it."

When the raft was loaded, it was towed slowly inch by inch behind one of our row-boats up to the beach. All the stuff was hauled off onto dry land and stored in a large tent which we had erected on the shore. When the last load had been brought over and the raft towed back to Keijo's wharf for the last time, Alan, who had done most of the heavy lifting, called for a holiday.

"I haven't had time to look at the place yet," he said. "Let's take a rest before we start building the house."

Next day found us all sprawled comfortably on the beach, surrounded by books, magazines and cushions and with the coffee-pot within easy reach. Keijo, rowing slowly past, looked stonily across the intervening water.

"You wasting time," he shouted. "You should working harder."

Alan, pulling at his pipe and flexing his tired muscles, watched him out of sight with narrowed eyes.

"Some day," he said darkly, "I'm going to take a poke at that guy."

"I've never seen him do any work yet," said Jerry. "All he wants to do is boss people who *are* doing it."

"Just wait, we'll show him a thing or two," I prophesied. "We'll have this house up before he knows what happened."

Next day we began the building of the log house which was to be our future home. With great ceremony, the foundation stone— or in this case, the foundation log—was laid, and we all gravely carved our initials into it.

Alan took over the job of tree felling and there was no chewing through them with the saw. He scorned such amateurish methods. The sound of the axe rang through the forest day and night, while trees crashed in all directions.

We noticed with secret satisfaction that although Alan's superior strength brought the trees down faster and more efficiently than we had done, he, like ourselves, seemed to have only the vaguest idea as to which way they would fall. For the first few days I was fully occupied in keeping myself and the dogs out of the way of danger. Suey, in particular, had a most disconcerting habit of appearing out of nowhere and sitting down in front of a tree which was just about to topple. We would give him up for lost when the tree fell heavily beside him and he was enveloped in the spreading green branches; but by some miracle, after the tremors had subsided, there would always be a small upheaval among the pine needles and a small, indignant head would poke through and glare defiantly around with an expression that seemed to ask, "Who done that?"

After studying the results of Alan's misplaced sense of direction for a few days, we came to the conclusion that a tree intended to fall to the right would inevitably fall to the left, and we disposed ourselves accordingly.

We built a primitive skid road on the hillside down which to shoot the logs from the upper reaches to the house site on the beach. The first log that journeyed down the new road took me along with it when the cuff of my glove caught in a projecting knot. We arrived at the bottom linked together, myself still miraculously in one piece.

"Great foolishness!" said Keijo, his eyes starting from his head as he watched from above.

"Anyone would think I did that on purpose," I snarled, looking up at him and rubbing my bruised legs.

Whenever Alan brought down a tree, Jerry and I, watching from a safe distance, ran up with our hatchets and draw-knives and started lopping off the branches, cutting away the top, and stripping off the soft, juicy bark. The long strips of bark peeled easily from the logs, and their beauty of colour and texture caused many interruptions in our work as we paused to admire and handle them.

"Wouldn't you think there would be a way of using anything as lovely as this?" asked Jerry, holding up a mottled ribbon of hemlock bark and turning it to show us the smooth red on the inner side.

"You can use it for making decorative panels on the walls of the house," answered Alan, who was artistically inclined; but the weeks went by and we were a long way from decorating the walls of the house, and the piles of strips dried and hardened in the sunshine and were finally used for kindling.

The building of the house was a much slower process than we had anticipated. We had no equipment for hoisting the logs, not even a block and tackle—nothing but our bare hands and our enthusiasm. Each log had to be sawn to the required length, notched at the end and laid in position, and the next log fitted snugly into the notch to make the saddle-and-rider corners. This meant several lift-ings off and on and much carving and fitting before the logs joined neatly.

The shorter logs we managed to get into position by the three of us standing astride them, taking a firm grip with our hands, and drawing a deep breath during the "One, two, three" which preceded the word "Heave!"; then, with every ounce of energy in us, lifting the log forward a foot or two at a time, until we had dragged it into the place where it was needed.

The thirty-four-foot logs of green fir which were to form the foundations of the house were a problem which taxed our strength and ingenuity to the utmost, the final result being achieved by the use of long cedar poles and a mysterious something called a "fulcrum."

Alan's glib use of this magic word left me with a feeling of awe and it was at least two days before I realized that a fulcrum was not a specialized name for the pole I was using.

We had other troubles too.

The rusty saws refused to cut, and we had no tools for sharpening them. The heads came off the hammers and we ran out of nails. This necessitated sending to town for more supplies, and during the resulting delay Jerry and I cast around for something else to do.

After some thought I decided to occupy my enforced rest by constructing one of those freakish pieces of architecture which seem to be a necessary adjunct to backwoods homes, and are popularly known as backhouses, outhouses, or, in less vulgar parlance, privies.

With unusual forethought we had brought up with us a chemical toilet, and a place to house it had become an urgent necessity.

While Jerry, weary of sleeping in a miasma of doggy exhalations, went to work on a kennel destined to hold the bride and her entire suite, I sallied forth with a light heart, a heavy hammer and a pocket full of assorted nails to construct a privy.

Some little distance from the house, I came upon a grove of young firs and, with what I considered a heaven-sent inspiration, decided to use the tree trunks as a framework. Returning to the cabin, I gathered all the odd lengths of board I could find, packed them up to the fir grove and, selecting four trees growing in some sort of a square, I proceeded to nail the assorted pieces of lumber from one tree to another.

The varying length and thickness of the boards made for a complete lack of uniformity in the walls. The nails split the thin boards and, not being long enough to go through the thick ones, left them hanging precariously from the tree trunks. Undismayed, I hammered diligently on until all the lumber was used up, which left me with two walls shoulder high and one that reached only to the waist. An ambitious attempt to make a thatched roof out of cedar boughs ended when the project collapsed around my neck, and I decided on the spot to copy the original plan of the chicken house and use a tarpaulin.

Having no door, I made a curtain out of two burlap sacks and draped it across the entrance. The result could not have been called a success by any stretch of imagination. The ragged sacks drooped forlornly in front, and from the sides and back it was quite evident that the head and shoulders of any person lunatic enough to use the place would be open to the world. In addition, whenever the wind swayed the trees, the whole building swayed with them in a most bilious manner.

Feeling the need of encouragement, I went in search of the others. Alan declared himself totally uninterested in amateur plumbing, and Jerry was deep in mathematical calculations relating to the height, width and depth necessary for a building intended to house four dogs.

Worn down by persistent urging, they finally consented to accompany me on a tour of inspection. It was a blowy day and the four young trees with the crazy construction nailed to them were rocking madly in the wind.

Alan gave one look and returned to the beach, shouting with laughter. I looked at my handiwork with some misgiving; somehow it did not seem to be such a success when viewed in a gale.

Jerry surveyed it from various angles, at the same time asking questions such as: "What happens to the privy when the trees grow up?"

My inability to answer this question satisfactorily brought about the surmise that the privy would probably grow up with the trees and in a couple of years we would be needing a stepladder to get into it.

The privy was regretfully torn down, and Jerry, her dog kennel having resolved itself into such a sorry sight that even the dogs passed it with averted looks, decided to take a hand at privy building herself.

The next privy took the shape of a lean-to attached to the cabin. It even had a roof, which leaked so badly that we had to patch it with old sacks and tarpaper; and eventually after much patching, it caved in altogether. One rainy day we discovered the roof of the privy reposing on the seat of the toilet, and the second privy went the way of the first.

By now, Alan had become infected with the privy-building fever, and the third one, result of our combined efforts, was a work of art. It actually stood on its own legs and did not have to lean against another building or rely on trees for its main support. We patronized it enthusiastically for a day or two, after which it collapsed completely as a result of one of Alan's misjudged tree-felling operations.

After that, the privy travelled unceasingly up and down the hillside as we each took turns at improving on the previous builder's style of architecture. One ambitious structure covered as much ground as a stable. The seat was wide enough and long enough to accommodate a double-bed spring, and furthermore had two holes in it, through either of which one could have driven a team of horses. There was no door, but by way of compensation Jerry ornamented the walls with large and expensive studio portraits of our friends and relations. On this occasion, Keijo was shocked to the point of displaying an unexpected streak of humour. Striding into the building and surveying the two gaping caverns in the seat, he remarked without a vestige of a smile, "You better putting on life preservers before you using that."

By way of contrast, the next building was so small that it was almost impossible to get in at all, but by economizing on wall space, we had enough lumber left over for a door—a door that refused to shut and had to be held in place by a length of twine attached to a nail on the inside and gripped firmly by the occupant.

"It is great foolishness to putting things up and then to taking them down," said Keijo, sternly disapproving.

"I know," I answered propitiatingly, "but we just don't seem to be able to find the right place for the beastly thing. It always seems to be in the way of something or other; but at least each time we build it it looks a little better."

"It looking terrible," grunted Keijo, morose and angry.

At last, after many takings down and puttings up, Alan found that he needed the lumber for something else, and the chemical toilet came to its final rest in a hollow tree. The remains of the burlap curtain were draped over it like a shroud, and with a rusty nail I carved out the letters R.I.P., which inscription Jerry interpreted to mean "Rust in Peace," a proceeding which was duly carried out.

With the passing of the chemical toilet passed the last of our civilized inhibitions, and we reverted to nature without any trouble at all.

"You know, it's funny how living this sort of life teaches you to distinguish between the important things and the unimportant," I said after we had buried the toilet. "I can remember when a house without full plumbing was a thing unheard of in respectable society, and a hot bath in the morning was something indispensable to decency. Now we find that a roof over one's head and food in one's stomach are the real basic necessities of life, and plumbing of any description is a complete superfluity."

By the time the privy-building mania had run its course, several kegs of nails had been dropped off by the weekly steamer and were brought in by the disapproving Keijo. Work on the log house was resumed.

"Nails. Nails. Always you wanting more nails," said Keijo in surly tones.

"Well, we can't build a house without them," said Jerry, prying the lid off one of the kegs.

"In my country we fastening logs together with wooden pegs."

"This isn't your country, we do things differently here."

"Always you wanting things easy," shouted Keijo angrily as he turned away.

"What's biting *him?*" inquired Alan, coming out from behind a pile of logs and mopping his perspiring brow.

Jerry looked after the departing Keijo.

"We're not doing things the hard way," she explained. "Instead of using nails, he thinks we should carve wooden pegs."

Alan's eyes bulged with horror at the bare idea.

"My God, what does he think we are?" He picked up the blunt cross-cut saw with a disgusted snort. "If he likes doing things the hard way, he should try using this."

Jerry frowned thoughtfully.

"I think it is time we began meeting the mail steamer ourselves. As long as we depend on Keijo for anything, we are giving him the right to criticize us. Besides, I want to find out what meeting the steamer is like. Next week, we will pick up our own mail."

Shortly after Alan's arrival, we had made the acquaintance of all four of the strong-and-silent men.

Emboldened by the sight of a man on the premises, they had rowed over to see us. They were four lean brown giants, shy and inarticulate and too overcome with embarrassment to be capable of personally offering their gifts of fresh vegetables and fish. We discovered these lying on the doorstep after they had gone.

Patient questioning had elicited the fact that the brothers had spent the greater part of their lives on the island. Their surname was Nelson. Orphaned by a logging-camp accident, they had obtained such education as they had through correspondence courses and their knowledge of the outside world was limited.

Besides 'Lias, there was Joel, the eldest of the four, a lanky six-foot-two, with a deeply lined face and premature streaks of grey in his black hair. Joel had taken the place of guardian to the other three.

In between 'Lias and Joel came Blackie, the shortest and most taciturn of the family, and last came Sonny, a clumsy young nineteen-year-old with wistful brown eyes and a most engaging grin.

In due course we had returned their visit, and gradually we had all come to be frequent guests in each other's houses.

The brothers owned ninety acres of bush and lived in a large two-storied house of their own building. On the occasion of our first visit, we were received in the thirty-foot living-room.

We looked about us covertly. The board floor was bare and scrubbed to a shining whiteness. There were one or two home-made wooden benches and chairs, a long trestle table covered with oilcloth, a couple of camp cots spread with grey army blankets, and an airtight heater from which a long black stove-pipe reared into the second storey, and from there, out through the roof.

Some attempt had been made at decoration. The walls were covered with coloured pictures cut from old magazines. There were curtains made from bleached flour sacks and a pickle jar filled with violets stood in the centre of the table.

We found our hosts attired in khaki shirts and trousers. The shirts were sleeveless and open at the neck, exposing a large expanse of hairy chest and arms.

I looked with awe at the massive muscles and began to feel my lack of inches acutely.

As we entered, we saw 'Lias sitting beside the stove working on a hooked rug.

"What are you doing?" I asked, coming towards him and surprised to find a man engaged in such a feminine occupation.

'Lias put aside the frame and rose to his feet. It seemed to me as if he would never stop rising. I looked up at him. Anything less feminine than his six feet of brawn and muscle and strong brown features could hardly have been imagined.

Evidently considering an answer to such an idiotic question

unnecessary, he merely smiled, and I knew how a Pomeranian feels when confronted with a friendly Great Dane.

We examined the house and the neatly joined logs with avid curiosity, exclaiming with admiration.

"Wooden pegs!" cried Jerry in stunned tones. "D'you mean to say that all the logs are fastened together with wooden pegs? Just think of the work! Why didn't you use nails?"

"Nails cost money," said Joel in his slow drawl. "Wood's free up here."

They showed us their smoke-house with the racks for drying fish and meat, and the animal haunches hanging from the smoke-blackened roof.

They showed us the new boat which they were building down on the beach. We looked at the primitive steam-box where the ribs of the boat were being bent into shape, and the planking they had cut out of tree trunks with rip-saws.

We looked at them with reverence.

"You did all this by yourselves? Cripes!"

We thought of our chicken house and privies; they suddenly seemed very poor things.

"I wish I could build a boat," said Jerry, looking with admiring eyes at the tall hull.

I thought of the home-made cake and raised biscuits they had offered us for tea, and I thought of the hooked rug, and felt unreasonably annoyed. Not only were we incapable of building a boat, but we were equally unable to bake raised biscuits or to hook rugs, and compared to their bare but well-scrubbed home, our cabin looked like a shambles.

I sighed, and looking up at them, said with the utmost sincerity: "How wonderful you are!"

A trite remark, which had probably never before been uttered with such sincerity and certainly never met with such a reaction.

The brothers almost swooned with embarrassment, and staring hard at their boots, flushed scarlet.

"You sure sounded silly," jeered Alan when we were rowing

home, "coming all over cute like that." Changing to a cracked falsetto, he echoed my unfortunate remark, "How wonderful you are!"

"Oh shut up! I wasn't trying to be cute. I think they really are rather wonderful. How many of the people we know could do all the things they do?"

Alan grew serious again.

"Wooden pegs! Hundreds of them! Kee-rist!"

Our resolve to pick up our own mail sent us calling again on the brothers for instructions.

'Lias and Joel listened gravely.

"There's no call for you to do that," said 'Lias. "We can always get your mail. It's liable to be rough out there and if you aren't used to handling a boat you might get into trouble."

On our insistence that we wished to be as independent as possible, they looked doubtfully at each other; then, shrugging their shoulders, they produced a tide book and Joel gave us full instructions on how to navigate the entrance channel.

"Wait for a slack tide," he said. "Keep as close to the sides as you can, the current isn't as strong there. When you get outside, head for the group of islands on your right and wait there. If it's rough, be sure and take the waves on the quarter. We'll look out for you."

Exhausted by this unusually long speech, Joel lit a cigarette and gazed over our heads into space.

We came away marvelling. Accustomed as we were to the nervous restlessness of city dwellers and their constant flow of inconsequential talk, the serene composure of the brothers was a never ending source of wonder and envy to us.

"It must be wonderful to be like that," I said and inwardly resolved to train myself to be cool, calm and collected under any circumstances.

My resolve was severely tested on our first trip out for the mail.

Following instructions, we had chosen our revolving skiff *Dizzy*

Lizzy for the adventure, Joel's opinion being that in spite of her waywardness she was a good sea boat.

Leaving Alan, whose experience of rapids-shooting on the day of his arrival had left him singularly disinclined for any similar adventures, we set forth with outward nonchalance and inward trepidation. After watching the fishing boat belonging to the brothers and Keijo's small power boat pass by on their way out, we scrambled into our skiff and followed in their wake.

By the time we had reached the entrance, our neighbours had outdistanced us and vanished seawards. The tide was rising fast and the rapids' turmoil was gently subsiding. After waiting for the last bubbles to disappear we floated through, disagreeably conscious of the hidden rocks beneath and oppressed by the steep walls on either side. Out in the open a slight choppiness caused *Dizzy Lizzy* to veer and lunge unpleasantly. Jerry, pulling at the oars, took a quick look over her shoulder.

"Those islands look a long way off," she remarked uneasily.

I gripped the sides of the boat with both hands and gave what I hoped was a reassuring smile.

"I can see some boats there, row-boats too. If they can make it, I guess we can."

Rising and falling on the waves and full of pride at what we considered to be our bravery, we drew up to the islands and the cluster of boats waiting there. 'Lias and Joel looked over the side of their boat as we approached and gave us an encouraging grin.

"I never thought we'd make it," I said and waited modestly for the applause due a heroine. Joel's calm rejoinder left me considerably dashed.

"Lucky you had such a calm day for your first try."

We made our first appearance at the meeting-place with some timidity, feeling that our invasion of this strictly masculine world might be resented. Uncertain of our reception, at first we kept our distance; but we soon found ourselves drawn into the genial comradeship that existed between the island residents. Although it apparently never occurred to our silent neighbours to make any formal introductions, we fell naturally into an easy fellowship with the fishermen, learning their names by hearing them when they spoke to each other.

After this first experience we made a regular practice of going out to meet the mail steamer, and as our initial fears wore off and we became used to handling the boat, we found ourselves looking forward eagerly each week to the arrival of mail day and the opportunity it afforded us for social contact with other people.

After years of having mail delivered to our door by a postman and never having done anything more arduous when mailing a letter than licking the stamp, it came as a surprise to us to find that receiving mail could be both a major event and an adventure.

The early-morning hours of mail day found us anxiously looking at the sky for signs of squally weather, studying the tide book and wrestling with mathematical computations relating to time and height of tides, and then comparing the result with the problematical schedule of the mail boat, whose hour of arrival could be anywhere between twelve noon and eight o'clock at night, depending on weather conditions, number of stops, and amount of freight to be delivered.

It was nothing out of the ordinary for the boat to be several hours late, and on more than one occasion it had neglected to stop at all, but had swept past in a flurry of waves, pursued by the furious maledictions of the islanders, who had been waiting out at sea for the better part of the day.

Fishing tackle and a supply of food were a necessary part of each boat's equipment.

The meeting-place for the boats was in the lee of a cluster of rocky islets, sheltered from the strong winds and the worst of the waves. To this spot an odd assortment of small craft used to creep out of little inlets and islands to wait patiently on an empty, heaving sea for the mail steamer which was their sole contact with the outside world.

Jerry and I, often the first to arrive, would watch them gather with the keenest interest. There were fishing boats, gliding silently out of hidden fjords like graceful white birds; row-boats, weather-beaten and lacking in paint; boats with small engines, boats with sails, all piloted by tanned, rugged individuals of various nationalities who had forsworn the noise, glare and high-powered automation of the modern world for the peace and serenity of sea and forest.

Among the regular members of the mail-day gathering was a battered-looking Irishman of uncertain age and antecedents who lived by himself on a nearby island and acted as postmaster for the scattered community. He always rowed standing up and wearing a high-crowned felt hat which he wore summer and winter. We were told that he had never been seen without it and all attempts to take him by surprise had proved to be completely fruitless. It did not matter what time of the day or night anyone called on Irish Pat, he always had his hat on.

"Faith, I was born in it," he replied when we ventured to question him on the matter.

Besides the postmaster, there was a handsome half-breed known as Big Pete. Pete was a guide, a trapper and a crack shot. His house was a museum of moose horns, grizzly-bear skins and other trophies. He also owned one of the best fishing boats on the coast. We gradually found out that his impressive height and brilliant blue eyes had been inherited from a Texan father. A Haida mother had bequeathed him striking Indian features and a dark skin, and his deep, rich voice and quiet self-possession probably stemmed from that same proud source.

There were two other fishing boats, belonging respectively to the four brothers, and to Christian, the blond Norse god who had met us on our arrival from the city.

Besides these larger vessels, there was a fleet of other boats, their owners more or less disreputable but colourful to an extreme. Among them was a one-eyed Swede, dour and suspicious, whose boat appeared to be in a perpetual state of leakage, a disadvantage which he had overcome by perfecting an elaborate technique which combined rowing with one hand and baling with the other.

The group was further augmented by an Icelandic fisherman, a tall, fair and utterly angelic-looking individual whose appearance completely belied his propensity for mischief. It was some time before we discovered his real name, and then finding it to be an impossible sound alternating between a hiss and a splash, we solved the problem of pronunciation by following the example set by the other men, and called him Yonnie.

There was a Norwegian mink farmer named Magnus who had a wooden leg and an addiction to "snoose" (Copenhagen snuff) and who spoke perfect and educated English. Another member of the group was Hans, a large jovial Dutchman whose hair shone in the sun like polished silver, and whose boisterous laugh rang out incessantly.

There was also a German who had taken an active part in a European holocaust, and in spite of its horrors still believed in war as a logical means of settling international disputes.

"War is a good thing," he said loudly during a heated discussion one day. "It gets the badness out of people and keeps the population down."

A statement against which there seemed to be no argument.

There were others—fishermen who came less often; lonely, uncommunicative men who came for a few weeks and then suddenly vanished. Naïve questionings concerning them elicited nothing but smiles and shrugs. The islanders were not troubled with curiosity.

One of the members of the group was a pale, quiet man who lived in an abandoned quarry on another island and suffered from a weak heart, an unpronounceable name, and a nationality unknown to everyone. His failure to show up for two mail days in succession led some of the fishermen to investigate, and his dead body was found lying on the quarry floor. On this occasion we discovered how little importance the islanders attached to death. One of the men sailed off to the nearest point on the mainland where there was a bush telephone and notified the police, who came in a motor launch and removed the body, and that was the end of the matter. Nobody mentioned him again or showed any interest in the few possessions he had left behind.

" He was a friend of yours, wasn't he?" I said reproachfully to Joel. "Don't you want to know what happened?"

"Why?" asked Joel indifferently. "He's dead, isn't he? Knowing what happened won't change that."

"I should think you would want to make sure that he was buried properly."

Joe hitched up his belt.

"Don't reckon they'll leave him rot in the street."

"What do you do when people die?" I questioned him. "Is there a cemetery here where they can be buried?"

There was an uncomfortable silence. Then the story came out bit by bit.

There *had* been a cemetery on the north end of the island. Digging a grave had been a voluntary task and posed something of a problem because the ground was all solid rock. The relations or friends of the deceased usually donated a few sticks of dynamite followed by a stiff tot of rum when the job was done, but many of the men were unused to handling dynamite and the shot of rum was found to be insufficient inducement to cause them to risk their lives digging a grave; so the price was upped, first to a half bottle, then, as the risks apparently increased, to a whole bottle. Finally the more avaricious resorted to wholesale blackmail and the cost of digging a grave mounted up to two bottles of rum and a case of blasting powder, any powder left over to be considered as a perquisite by the diggers and used for blowing out wells and stumps on their own property.

From then on grave-digging became a popular and riotous pastime.

The end of the idyll came when two of the amateur grave-diggers, overcome by the combination of blasting powder and rum, had blasted themselves out of existence, and the cemetery had been closed.

"What do you do now?" I asked, striving to keep a straight face.

"There's a buryin'-ground over on the mainland," said one of the men unwillingly, "but we don't use it no more."

Blackie took up the tale.

It appeared that this "buryin'-ground" was located in a swamp and although the digging was easy, the wet weather caused the holes to fill up with water faster than they could be baled out. I was treated to a macabre and colourful description of an occasion when a coffin had been dropped into a grave with a loud splash and had promptly bobbed up to the surface again like a cork.

"We had to heave rocks on her to hold her down while we filled in the hole," ended Blackie in tones of disgust. "Hell—it's bad enough being buried without being drowned into the bargain."

Further questions failed to bring up any more information on burying, and we were forced to the conclusion that the islanders, faced with the horrors of a swamp burial, had given up dying.

As each boat arrived at the cluster of rocky islands, it was greeted with shouts of welcome, and willing hands tied up the smaller craft to one of the anchored fishing boats while the occupants climbed aboard the bigger vessels to sit about on deck and discuss the doings of the week. Keijo, who believed in wasting no time in useless talk, was the only one who kept aloof from the friendly group, and sailing about in one of his own creations, occupied himself with his fishing-lines, his back turned very pointedly in our direction.

On sunny days we lay face down on the warm decks gazing dreamily at the blue mountains showing faintly through their drifting veils of mist, and at the little rocky islands lifting their skirts of brown seaweed out of the water.

The smell of tar oozing up between the deck planks mingled with a faint scent of spruce blown to us from the shore, and all around us the sea shimmered in the heat haze.

Physically and mentally relaxed, we were conscious of a sense of contentment such as we had never experienced before.

When the weather was cold and wet, we sat in the ship's cabins in a fog of tobacco smoke and wet, steaming clothes. While the boats heaved slowly up and down in the ground swell and the coffee-pots bubbled on the tiny stoves, we listened to discussions carried on in a variety of different accents. We heard the harsh gutturals of the

Dutch and Germans, the accented sibilants of the Scandinavians, and the cultured and gentle voices of Big Pete and Magnus.

We picked up a lot of assorted information on logging and fishing and came to know the meaning of such terms as "spar trees," "widowmakers" and "schoolmarms." A "widowmaker," we were informed, was a name applied to a loose branch which had been caught up in the high branches of another tree. Magnus's brother had been killed by a "widowmaker" falling on his head as he passed beneath it.

The "schoolmarm" turned out to be a tree that had branched out into two separate trunks. How the term came to be applied to such an object we never did find out.

We also learned the names of the different kinds of salmon—the coho, spring, hump, and sockeye—and how to distinguish between them. We were shown a sea cucumber and instructed in the Japanese method of cooking it so that it tasted like chicken.

"Not for me, thank you," said Jerry, shuddering. "It looks like a big slug."

"If you are hungry enough, you don't think about how a thing looks," smiled Magnus.

We were also told about, and warned against, the infamous "sea blubber," a huge red jellyfish that grew to six or eight feet in diameter and had long poisonous tentacles that caused excruciatingly painful rashes and in some cases death. Hauling in our lines one day, we found them covered with blood-red jelly.

"Don't touch it," cried Magnus, "it's sea blubber. If you get that on your hands and happen to rub your eyes, it could make you blind."

I shuddered and hastily rinsed my hands in the sea.

"Do these horrible things ever come to the surface?" I asked.

"Sometimes—in rainy weather," said Magnus. "Just be careful to wash that stuff off your lines and if you ever see one rise, keep away from it."

Among other things, we discovered the origin of the old superstition that forbids the eating of shellfish in months that have no *r* in them.

"Most superstitions are based on fact," explained Magnus. "Have you ever heard of the Red Tide?"

We had not.

"It's an alga that appears sometimes and poisons the shellfish. All the Indians know about it and recognize it when it comes, but for people who don't know enough to notice the red tinge in the sea at these times, the best thing is to follow the old rule and don't eat shellfish during the forbidden months."

Magnus opened the lid of his snuffbox thoughtfully.

"People think it's smart to laugh at what they call 'old wives' tales'," he said, "but there was a certain amount of truth in them all the same."

Conversation on a more intellectual level was lacking and international politics were treated with a hearty contempt by the islanders, who regarded all forms of government with a thorough-going distrust. To them, a government meant an evil abstraction that detracted considerably from their way of life by interfering with what they considered the perfectly legitimate business of shooting deer out of season, operating stills, "pitlamping," and other such harmless pursuits. ("Pitlamping" is hunting by night with a miner's lamp strapped to the forehead. The light attracts the deer, is reflected in their eyes, and makes them an easy target. It is strictly against the law.)

Looking at their impassive faces and being female and inquisitive, we often attempted to draw them out into talking about their own countries and homes, but we were always met with a wall of reserve. Their past was not a subject for open discussion.

"We might as well all be in the French Foreign Legion," I said to Jerry. "Nobody knows anything about anybody here."

Profiting by the instruction of these seasoned seamen, we became expert at handling a boat. We soon found out the trick of pulling up beside a fishing boat which was rolling in a high sea, tossing the mooring rope to waiting hands, and leaping aboard as we rose on the crest of a wave. We learnt the art of tacking and how to splice a rope and, as we gradually lost all fear of the sea, we found an increasing fascination in all its various moods. There were days when the water was glassy calm, and days when it was a sullen, heaving grey hidden by driving rain, and there were times when under a stiff westerly breeze it took on the colour of jade topped with flying white scud; and always it was beautiful.

The long hours of waiting for the steamer never brought that state of fretful tedium with which we had been so familiar in the city. When conversation languished, everyone sank into a contemplative mood and with eyes glued to the horizon, seemed to lapse into a state of suspended animation.

In a little while we found ourselves following the example set by the others and passing into a dreamlike calm which was broken only by the warning blast of the steamer as it approached.

On the days when the ship had been delayed by an unusually heavy delivery of freight, the sun would often be sinking into the sea before it appeared off the islands. A chill wind springing up would cause the men to huddle into their heavy jackets and look uneasily at the sky. Slowly the steamer turned in towards us and the sound of her siren reverberated among the mountains.. With the appearance of the steamer a great activity broke out among the waiting boats. The owners of the small craft scrambled back into their own places. Anchors were hauled up, oars creaked in oarlocks, ropes were cast off, and sudden spurts of life came from the gas engines as the islanders moved out to meet the mail boat.

Irish Pat, in his role of postmaster, led the way, rowing forward with his slow easy sweep and his big hat tilted over his eyes, and behind him wavered a long trail of different-sized boats.

The steamer slowed down and turned to make a lee for the small vessels struggling towards her across the open water. The rail was crowded with curious passengers leaning down to watch the proceedings. The big double doors of the freight deck were thrown open and the islanders drew up one by one and had their crates and packages handed down to them by the deck hands. On rough days, the bringing of the fishing boats up against the side of the heaving steamer was a difficult task. There were broken oars and broken boat hooks, freight lost overboard, and a picturesque variety of language as deck-hands and fishermen alike fought to keep their plunging boats from crashing together.

On these occasions we often waited in the lee of the islands and let the owners of the bigger boats collect our freight. With all our love of the sea we had retained a healthy respect for it in its stormier moods, and Joel's curt "Don't come. We'll get your mail" was a warning that was never delivered unnecessarily.

When the last of the packages had been loaded on the boats, the freight doors were closed. The steamer sounded a farewell note and turned away into the dusk, and the islanders returned to the shelter of the rock islands where for a moment all was confusion as Pat emptied the mail sacks and distributed letters and papers.

Our mail was always a heavy one and often I felt a guilty pang when I met the wistful and anxious eyes of some lonely soul who had rowed patiently out week after week without receiving so much as a mail-order catalogue.

Pat's folding of the mail sacks and the words "That's all" were the signal for the group to begin melting away in different directions. The larger boats frequently gave a tow to smaller ones. Last messages were called across ever widening patches of water. An anxious look at the sky and a "Better hurry up, she's going to blow" to some belated straggler would cause us to put a little more energy into our rowing; then the engines' thudding would echo and die away among the mountains and in a little while there would be nothing left but the grey empty sea and the gathering night.

Mail day was over for another week.

Chapter 5

Spring began to melt imperceptibly into summer. The walls of the log house crept up slowly and spaces for windows and doors began to appear as a result of Alan's industry.

Our food supplies still continued to arrive by mail steamer, to Keijo's great disgust. To order by mail instead of growing our own produce he considered to be a direct cheating on life lived the hard way, and his fury knew no bounds when he discovered that we were buying peat moss, mash, and crushed oyster shell for the chickens.

"They no needing it," he raved. "You letting them loose—they feeding themselves."

Cowed by the fire in his eyes, we allowed ourselves to be persuaded, left the door of the chicken yard open, and to our surprise found that Keijo was right. The hens wandered about in the forest feeding on insects and weeds, and picked up their own shell on the beach. All we had to do was throw out a handful of wheat night and morning and spread sand on the floor of the chicken house.

The yolks of the eggs turned from an anaemic yellow to a deep orange. The flavour improved and the cost of the feed dropped.

"Now they are living the hard way too," I said.

"Now they are living the right way," answered Keijo.

The dogs' diet of canned horse meat also came in for a drastic change. Fish heads and clams were boiled together until they were soft, mixed with oatmeal into a thick porridge, and served to the hungry animals once a day. There were no complaints from this quarter, and judging by the glossy coats and lively spirits the change was an improvement.

Our few attempts at fishing had not proved very successful. The fishermen grinned slyly at our fancy rods and tackle, and we found that the one-eyed Swede with a few hundred feet of "cuttyhunk" (heavy green fishing-line) wound round a stick of stove wood and weighted with a handful of rusty nails, caught more fish than we did with all our expensive equipment. In spite of this we never went short of fish. The members of the mail-day gathering kept us well supplied, and even the stranger fishermen would often drop a small salmon into our boat in an unobtrusive manner when we came out for the mail.

Freed from the worry of a flood of monthly bills, we found that a very little money went a long way. There was no rent; there were no bills for light, telephone, fuel, transportation, or gasoline; there were no stores to tempt us into rash spending. After the feverish rush of city life, we found ourselves sinking into a serene state of mind which was as pleasant as it was unusual.

Among our friends we began to notice an air of restlessness, though. The busy season was on its way and the talk was all of possible bumper garden crops and what the chances were of a good fishing season.

Fishing boats began to blossom out in new coats of paint. Nets were put to soak in bluestone tanks, and while waiting for the mail the men would be busy at odd repair jobs on their boats. Visiting from one boat to another, we had plenty of opportunity to inspect the gear and equipment and to marvel at the dexterity with which the little vessels were handled.

None of the boats were over thirty feet in length, and most of them were a bare eight feet in width. The wheel-house and the cabin were all up in front, leaving the back of the boat clear for deep fish hatches. When the vessel was equipped for fishing, every inch of space was filled with lines, nets, and markers. The markers were either shaped like big blue balloons, or were yellow kidney-shaped bladders which the fishermen called "pigs." The men, amused by our interest, sometimes took us for short runs in their boats and we stood in the bows feeling the deck lift under our feet as the sharp prow cut through the waves, and the cold spray blew into our faces. We raised and lowered the long trolling poles, twisted the net drums on the gill-netters, and were showed how the electric "gurdys" pulled in the lines.

We examined the bait boxes in the rear and the cramped living-quarters in front. On one boat, the owner's bunk was built into the wheel-house. It was lined with foam rubber and the blankets were of fine lambswool.

I fingered the outer side of the bunk, which could be raised or lowered at will—"So I won't fall out when it's stormy," explained the fisherman.

"Who steers the boat when you're asleep?"

He explained the automatic pilot that kept the boat on course.

"We don't sleep much," he said. "When the fish are running we are too busy. The man who stops to sleep or rest catches no fish."

"How far do you go?" inquired Jerry, looking at the stained and yellow charts.

"Depends—we follow the fish. Sometimes the run is close in, sometimes we have to go miles out to sea, sometimes away up north where the bad storms are and the freezing rain ices up the deck and the boat rolls so you can't keep a pan on the stove."

I shuddered and looked at the unconcerned fisherman with respect.

"Wouldn't logging be a safer way of making a living?" I asked. The fisherman laughed.

"I have worked in the camps," he said. "They are not safe either, and when it comes to dying—well, the sea is kinder than the woods."

He turned the boat back to the islands and pressed the button that set the depth-sounder in action.

I watched fascinated as a red flame sprang into life on the dial, spreading and flickering across the face of the sounder as the boat moved across shallows and reefs, and dwindling to a tapering vertical line as the water deepened.

"The numbers on the dial show the depth of the water—show where the fish are, too."

As we approached the islands the depth-sounder flickered wildly, then went dark as the fisherman snapped off the switch. The engine gave a grinding roar as it was thrown into reverse and the boat came to a standstill. Running catlike along the narrow deck, he dropped the anchor over the bows and came slowly back to where we stood at the wheel-house door.

The Dutchman, watching us from the deck of his own boat, cupped his hands round his mouth and roared in booming tones: "You come feeshing wit' us—you haff plenty foon bigosh."

Looking across at his brown, cheerful face, I found myself for the first time in my life deploring a fate that had decreed me to be born female.

On our next trip out for the mail, we saw the first of the fishing fleet going up north to the fishing-grounds. These were the trollers, always the first to go. We watched them sail by in twos and threes, sometimes linked together as if arm in arm, their slender prows slicing through the waves and their tall, raking poles rocking against the grey sky.

The islanders looked after them as a captive swan might watch the migrating flight of its kind, and the following week the mail-day assembly had shrunk to half its number. Gone were the Dutchman, the homesick Icelander, and the German; gone were the nameless and transient men who had wintered in the calm bays and inlets. We were left with the Nelson brothers, Keijo, an odd trapper or two, and the gill-netters, already chafing with impatience and eager to follow the others.

"What is this fever that makes men so anxious to follow the fish?" I asked Magnus. "According to them, it's dangerous, uncomfortable and often unprofitable, but they still go. Isn't there something else they can do?"

Magnus took a pinch of "snoose" from a round tin and packed it under his upper lip meditatively.

"To some men the very danger is an attraction," he said. "Then there is a comradeship among fishermen which you don't find in other jobs; and of course, there is always the possibility that this season will be the year of the big run when everyone will make a fortune."

His eyes wandered off to the dark line of the horizon. "It's a seasonal thing too; a man doesn't have time to get bored the way an office worker does. However hard or unprofitable the season has been, he has the whole winter in which to forget it, and with the spring comes a fresh run of fish and a fresh hope."

With the departure of the fishermen went one of the main topics of conversation—fishing—and the attention of the remaining residents turned almost exclusively to gardening.

"When you digging garden?" inquired Keijo one day.

"Garden? Oh yes, the garden," I replied vaguely. "I really hadn't thought about it."

"Time you thinking," commented Keijo.

"I suppose we should," I said later to Jerry, "everyone else is doing it." But time went on and, occupied with the house building and realizing the extreme limitations of our gardening knowledge, we neglected to dig the garden. One day when visiting our silent neighbours we were arrested by the sight of the rows of seedlings coming up in their own neat vegetable garden.

We stopped and looked with admiration at the sight.

"Just look at all that corn coming up," said Jerry, "and the potatoes and things!"

The brothers followed the direction of our gaze.

"That's spinach," said 'Lias uncomfortably, "the spuds are over in the far end."

"Can you eat it now?" I asked.

"Reckon not," answered 'Lias, "but there's some radishes coming up you might try."

He pulled up half a dozen tiny scarlet balls and, gravely wiping the soil off on his sleeve, handed them to us.

Jerry bit into one tentatively and her eyes widened.

"Why, they don't taste a bit like the ones you buy in the stores," she said.

"We've never eaten a store one," said Joel. "What do they taste like?"

"Wood, mostly," I said, chomping enthusiastically; then, turning to Jerry, I added with conviction: "We have got to have a garden, a real vegetable garden with peas and squash growing in soil instead of in cans."

"Wa-a-al," said Joel, hitching up his belt, "now's the time to be planting if you aim to get any vegetables this year."

So while the log house progressed slowly under Alan's hands, Jerry and I took time off to prepare our vegetable garden. From an ancient seed catalogue we made out a fantastic order. Driven slightly demented by the gorgeous illustrations, we listed large quantities of muskmelon, egg-plant and others of the more exotic plants, and added small amounts of carrots and turnips and the more common vegetables, for which we had not much partiality. Young fruit trees, blackberry vines, and raspberry canes were ordered, and as a final glorious touch we bought a fig tree.

"You're nuts," said Alan with a contemptuous snort. "Figs won't grow here."

"It said in the catalogue that this is a special kind of fig guaranteed to grow in Canada."

"Maybe, but not out of solid rock in the middle of a primeval forest."

"Well," I answered comfortably, "even if it doesn't have any figs, it will look pretty."

While waiting for the order to arrive, we selected a piece of flat ground near the lake and cleared, dug and fenced it; and here we delved, raked and planted with all the ardour born of ignorance.

Bracken and wild grass were torn up, and the whole plot dug into rows of deep trenches at the bottom of which we hopefully scattered the seeds. Young cauliflower, cabbage and tomato plants donated by the Nelsons were buried up to the neck in the gravelly soil, and two sacks of seed potatoes were sunk. The vines and fruit trees were set in with some difficulty, for the roots of the great forest trees that surrounded the garden plot stretched so far that wherever we attempted to dig, we seemed to run into them.

"Let's just set them on the surface and pile soil over the roots, then in time they can find their own way down," said Jerry. "These great big pines don't seem to have any trouble, why should a dwarf apple have any?" The planting finished, we leaned blissfully on our spades and dreamed rosy dreams of summer salads.

My imagination, running riot, pictured spires of golden corn, fat green peas and luscious red tomatoes running wild all over the rock-strewn ground and in my mind's eye I could see the fruit trees dripping with apples and cherries. In one last burst of fancy I saw myself astounding Alan with a purple fig modestly offered—sliced—for breakfast.

"This is virgin soil," I said happily. "We ought to get some marvellous crops."

My dreams of summer salads faded away as the weeks passed and the vegetable garden continued to turn a dry and barren surface up to the spring sunshine. The soil lived up to its reputation for virginity by being completely unproductive, and all that resulted from our labours were some sallow shoots where the early potatoes had been planted, a few anaemic carrots, and a fine crop of stunted bracken.

"The place needs water," said Alan, scuffing the dusty ground with the toe of his boot. "How do you expect to grow anything in this? It needs fertilizer too."

We walked dolefully round the garden.

The fruit trees stood stark and leafless, the rhubarb crowns were black and dry, the blackberry vines hung lifeless on the fence, and our expensive raspberry canes were withered.

"I don't think it pays to grow vegetables," I said ruefully, plucking a handful of famished-looking carrots. "When you think of the cost of the seed and the plants and then all the work you have to do, digging, you are better off buying them in cans."

"Rubbish!" said Jerry with energy. "Other people round here grow vegetables; there's no reason why we shouldn't. It just needs a little practice, that's all."

Spurred on by Jerry's determination, I picked up my spade and we set to work redigging and replanting the garden.

Profiting by our past mistakes and the advice of the brothers, we confined our amateur efforts to the more homely of the vegetable family and wasted no more time and money on egg-plant and fig trees.

We poured rivers of water over the land. Stones, which seemed to come up fresh with every shower of rain, were carefully picked off. Wilting under the roars of rage with which Keijo greeted our proposed purchase of chemical fertilizer and the discovery that he operated on the European theory that the best fertilizer for vegetables was the contents of the family privy, we used the scrapings from the chicken house and sacks of seaweed laboriously gathered from the rocks on the beach and packed up the hill, thinking all the while with shudders of Sundi's green salads and vowing never to be tempted into eating any more of Keijo's vegetables, "—though there really isn't any difference between chicken manure and the human variety," I said, in a vain attempt to be logical.

"None at all," said Jerry, "except that human manure is a lot more personal, somehow."

Jerry, in her first enthusiasm, rowed daily to Keijo's homestead and brought back buckets full of liquid manure from the cow barn which she poured lavishly over the soil, until, returning from one trip, she fell over a large root, and poured the contents of the bucket over herself. After that the liquid manure was rationed to one bucket a week, doled out with an old teaspoon to the most needy of the plants.

As soon as the seeds began to come up, excitement was intense;

every individual plant had its own name and special brand of treatment.

"Cabbage number three from the end prefers his chicken soup diluted, so be careful not to overdo it," warned Jerry as I went the rounds with a bucket of manure and the watering-pot.

"Bless his little heart, I believe he knows me. Just look at him peeping at me from under the leaves"—uncovering something which bore a suspicious resemblance to a gangrened appendix.

"What on earth is it?"

"A CUCUMBER! A real cucumber!" came in tones of ecstasy.

Keijo, who was kept up to date on all our doings by his wife, turned up his nose in scorn when informed of the vegetables we were raising, and was understood to say that people who took time off every afternoon to swim and drink tea would never raise any vegetables worth looking at.

"I always working in garden six—seven—maybe eight hours a day—maybe more," he said loftily to us; but Sundi, who was growing more self-assertive under our corrupting influence, murmured under her breath, "Don't take any notice of him—he crazy. I hoeing potatoes—he eating them."

Joel and 'Lias, on their visits of inspection, lounged indolently against the fence, and leaning their folded arms on the top rail watched us approvingly.

"You're doing fine," they said. "We never thought you would get any vegetables at all, the way you started off."

Warmed by their encouragement, we hoed regularly, and in spite of such difficulties as virgin soil and plain ignorance, our vegetables grew. We forsook the lagoon and the boats rocked undisturbed in the shallow waters off the beach while we spent long, dim evenings watering the struggling plants and staking up the weaklings; and in that quiet garden, sheltered from winds by the tall forest trees and away from the noise of the sea, we sat when darkness had fallen and felt the silence about us and spoke in hushed tones of the miracle which was happening before our eyes. The miracle which transforms a small brown seed into a living green plant.

94

Our next experiment was not such a satisfactory one. It involved the purchase of a goat named Fanny, and was the cause of a rift between Keijo and ourselves which widened considerably as time went on.

The goat was the natural outcome of all the dairy equipment which we had brought with us. Jerry, coming across it one day, all piled up in its shining newness, decided that the time was ripe for the purchase of a goat.

"That means another shed to be built for her," I objected, my mind revolting against the thought of more days filled with fulcrums and "one-two-three-heaves."

Jerry brushed my objections aside.

"Pooh! We built a chicken house, didn't we?" she said airily.

"I still think that canned milk is less trouble," I said grumpily.

"People don't pioneer on canned milk. We said we would have a goat and by golly, we're going to have a goat."

I resigned myself to the inevitable and, in between watering the garden and helping Alan to roll logs to the walls of the new house and set them in position, we set to work designing a goat house for the new prospective member of the community.

For once, we exercised a little forethought in choosing a site for the goat shed, and built it on a level place that did not require much clearing.

The dressed lumber by now had all been used up, so the walls of the goat house were constructed of the top half of trees left over from the building of the log house, stripped of their branches and standing upright. The roof was covered with old boards torn from an abandoned trapper's hut which we had discovered on the other side of the lagoon, and the resulting effect would have haunted an architect's dreams forever.

We had no hinges for the door, so we made some out of strips of leather cut from an old boot. Two apple boxes nailed to the wall served as a feed trough, and the goat house was finished.

The news that we were in the market for goats began to get around by that mysterious grapevine that exists in out-of-the-way places, and one mail day a passing fishing boat brought us the news that a farmer in a small settlement further up the coast had a goat which he was willing to sell cheap.

Negotiations were opened and presently we received a letter from the farmer stating the price and containing a description of the proposed purchase: Fanny, according to the letter, was "one week fresh."

Not being very well versed in barnyard talk, we were left gaping by this remark.

"Fresh?" queried Jerry.

"That's what it says here."

We discussed the word and its possible implications without arriving at any satisfactory conclusion, and I returned to the letter.

"He wants twenty bucks for the goat and two kids. Isn't that rather a lot?" I asked cautiously.

Jerry produced a pencil and paper and proceeded to work out some involved arithmetical problems concerning the price of lamb per pound and the problematical weight of a goat.

After a considerable amount of figuring, and taking into consideration the fact that we were acquiring a milk supply in addition to a large quantity of meat on the hoof, we decided that the price was reasonable.

The bargain was clinched and we joyfully spread the floor of the goat house with dried bracken and filled up the feed box with oats in preparation for the advent of Fanny.

Mail day came. Keijo, intrigued in spite of himself at this latest example of "great foolishness," took Jerry out in his power boat to meet the new arrivals.

It was several hours before they returned, during which time I impatiently walked up and down the beach and made several excursions to the entrance to look for them. At last I heard the sound of Keijo's motor echoing back and forth between the hills as it came up the lagoon. Standing on the beach I watched them ride up. Jerry, standing in the bows, was attempting to hold down two large wooden crates which under the antics of their occupants were heaving violently up and down. Keijo, for once showing some sense of humour, was sitting in the stern, both hands in the air and going through all the motions of an imaginary milking.

I jumped up and down with excitement as the boat drew in to shore and Alan left his tree felling and came down to the beach with an anticipatory grin on his face.

The crates were carefully lifted out.

The first, when opened, disclosed a tangle of legs and horns which when sorted out resolved themselves into a tiny doe and a baby billy-goat.

In the other crate was Fanny.

She was an unprepossessing sight. Her long yellowish-white coat was matted and dirty. Her ribs were sprung and one leg had a festering sore on it. Above all, she had a beery grin and a malicious gleam in her eye that boded no good for anyone.

"H'm," said Alan, looking critically at her rear end, "if you get any milk out of that old girl I'll be surprised."

"Why?" I asked. "The letter said she had a large udder and teats that just cleared the ground. That's good, isn't it?"

Alan gave a snort of laughter.

"Just wait till she starts trailing that contraption of hers over these old roots and stumps. You're going to spend your life picking wood splinters out of it."

Keijo looked at our crestfallen faces with a smirk of satisfaction.

"She plenty old," he said. "It is great foolishness to buying old animal like this. You should buying cow."

Jerry turned on him with angry eyes.

"How do you know we won't get any milk?" she demanded. "We haven't tried yet."

At this, Keijo and Alan remembered urgent business elsewhere and Jerry and I were left face to face with the milking problem.

"Who's going to milk her?" I asked.

"I am," declared Jerry stoutly.

"All right, let's see you do it," I jeered.

A brand-new pail was produced from the storehouse and between us we led the reluctant goat up to the shed and pushed her by main force onto the milking platform. From the beginning it was evident that in the battle between extraction and retention, Fanny was going to be the victor.

After a series of coy starts and head-tossings, she went into a complicated and thunderous tap dance with all four feet. The milking platform swayed ominously.

Jerry advanced a timid hand towards Fanny's rubbery appendage and commenced pulling.

"Hold her front feet," she ordered, hauling ineffectually with both hands, "hold her back feet—get an armlock on her—do *something*, for heaven's sake. You're not a bit of use. . . . Get up, you giddy old idiot"—to Fanny, who was endeavouring to sit down in the milk pail.

I hurled myself on Fanny and clung desperately round her neck while she sucked mouthfuls of my hair.

The combination of frontal attack and rearguard action brought results and a thin stream of milk squirted musically against the side of the pail.

"Milk! Just look at the milk!" cried Jerry in ecstasy.

I turned my head and looked with interest. Fanny, for the moment freed from restraint, executed a perfect *entrechat* and came down with both hind legs in the bucket.

Jerry turned an angry face towards me.

"I thought I told you to hold on," she said furiously.

We threw ourselves on Fanny in a combined attack and for the next few minutes the air rang with indignant bleatings and stampings punctuated by a lot of "Oh Fannies" and "Ah Fannies" and "What the hell Fannies." The frightened squawks of the chickens in a nearby pen added to the general clamour, and the uproar was topped off by the tremulous cries of the kids and the frenzied barks of the dogs, who were racing in a state of delirium round the milking platform.

The proceedings were brought to an untimely end by the collapse of the platform, which precipitated the whole works to the ground, and the net result of our first milking added up to one completely demoralized goat, two disillusioned farmerettes, and one badly dented bucket containing half an inch of very dirty milk.

"Oh my!" cried Jerry, holding her head in both hands. "To think we have to go through this twice a day!"

"I don't think we will need to, judging by the amount of milk," I replied, peering critically into the bucket. "About once a month ought to do."

The next few days proved the truth of the assertion that we would get no milk from Fanny. The kids had evidently been born of another mother, and Fanny was drier than a desert. We shame-facedly had to admit that we had been swindled and that instead of being an asset, Fanny was going to be a liability. As the days passed, she threatened to become an expensive one. Her appetite was enormous and her temper was vile. If we tied her up, she immediately proceeded to walk round and round the tree to which she was tied, twisting the rope into impossible knots and filling the air with persistent and rowdy squawks until, for the sake of peace, we had to leave whatever we were doing and go to her assistance. The sight of us hurrying towards her always brought about a complete cessation of the squawks and produced instead a grin of the most diabolical delight.

"Let the beast loose," said Alan. "Maybe she'll get lost."

Giving Fanny her freedom brought about another set of prob-lems. She butted her ugly head against everything in sight. The fence round the chicken run was brought down in ruins, and from then on, one of our main troubles was how to keep the livestock out of the house. Short of keeping the door shut and allowing the cabin to become suffocatingly hot, there seemed to be no way of keeping Fanny outside where she rightly belonged and off our beds, which she had decided were a lot more comfortable than the straw in the goat house.

Meals were eaten with four pairs of doggy eyes fixed greedily on us, Fanny leering round the door-post, the baby goats sitting on our laps, and a horde of hungry chickens running in and out under the table picking up the crumbs. Eating was punctuated on our part by constant jumpings up and yellings of "Shoo!" or a more violent equivalent.

"Damn it all! Can't you do something about these animals? It's like living in a stable," cried Alan one day on coming in for lunch and finding the chairs all occupied by hens.

"Just be thankful we haven't got a cow," replied Jerry, chasing Fanny off her bed and going round with a mop and shovel.

Things reached a grand climax when Fanny made the discovery that by taking a tortuous route across the hills and through the forest, it was possible to reach Keijo's vegetable garden; and from then on life brightened considerably for her and struck a new low for us.

Once she had tasted fresh green vegetables, there was no holding Fanny, and as it was impossible for us to follow her twisting trails through the dense bush, rowing up the lagoon to Keijo's farm and bringing the delinquent back by boat became a regular occurrence.

Inducing Fanny to enter a row-boat was a herculean task. It took the combined efforts of both Jerry and myself to drag her forcibly out of Keijo's asparagus bed and down to the beach. Once there, the sight of the boat seemed to do something drastic to her morale, and she sat back on her haunches pulling away from it with all her might, while Jerry and I, each with one hand gripping her collar, reached vainly with the other towards the boat, trying to connect the two.

Sometimes during the struggle Fanny's collar broke, and it would be our turn to sit back suddenly on our haunches while Fanny loped off into the asparagus again.

The battle generally ended when Keijo, fire blazing in his eyes, took a hand and dumped our evil genius bodily into the boat, holding her down despite her yells and struggles until we had climbed in and taken over.

Wilting under Keijo's justifiable rage, we rowed home, Fanny's feet beating a tattoo on the bottom of the boat, and her frustrated bleats echoing from one shore to the other.

One day she disappeared.

We searched the acreage, calling her by name; we struggled over her self-made trails and climbed the rocky hills without seeing a sign of her. We called on Keijo to see if she had been ravaging his vegetable garden recently; surly and uncommunicative, he shook his head without looking up from what he was doing.

Fanny had simply gone and left no trace.

Half-way between worry and relief, we continued our search until at last we were forced to confess ourselves beaten.

The Nelsons were consulted.

"Maybe a grizzly got her," I said, my mind refusing to accept repeated assurances that grizzlies were seen only in the high mountains of the mainland.

'Lias gave a short laugh.

"I wouldn't be surprised," he said drily, "and I think your grizzly has blue eyes and speaks Finn."

Several weeks passed before we accidentally came across all that was left of Fanny. Her mangled and water-soaked body was lying in a deep gully between two rocky peaks on the shoreline, too far down for us to get to her. We could only look and speculate as to what had happened.

"She slip," said Keijo when brought reluctantly to the scene.

"Nonsense, goats don't slip," I retorted crisply.

A faint gleam showed in Keijo's eyes.

"This one slipping," he said.

Next day we questioned 'Lias again.

"*Could* a goat slip?" I asked.

"It could," said 'Lias, carefully rolling a neat cigarette, "—with a bullet in it."

"Jolly good riddance," said Alan gruffly. "If Keijo shot her, he deserves a vote of thanks."

Jerry and I made one last sentimental journey for a final look at the corpse. It was high tide and the sea had filled the gully, but far below we could see the long hair of Fanny's coat stirring in the green water and her head seemed to nod gently.

"Poor Fanny!" I said regretfully.

"Poor nothing!" replied Jerry indignantly. "That will teach her not to steal asparagus."

With this brief funeral oration, we turned away and left Fanny to the slow disintegrating forces of the sea and air.

After our experiences with Fanny, it was only natural that the two kids should be christened "Horrible" and "Terrible," but we found that they failed to live up to the ominous nature of their names.

"Terrible," the billy-goat, was a sturdy, affectionate little beast with a long silky coat which we groomed daily; but as poor "Horrible" grew, it became increasingly evident that the mainland farmer had done us in again. The animal was a deformed little creature, delicate and complaining. Keijo, with an eye to future ravages on his asparagus, spoke glowingly of the tastiness of roast kid.

"They being no good except for eating," he said. "I shooting them for you."

"You'll do no such thing," I said angrily, cuddling the crippled doe. "They get on wonderfully with the dogs and we are going to keep them for pets."

On this occasion, Keijo's opinions regarding our "great foolishness" scared the seagulls off the beach.

Meanwhile the vegetable garden produced. The hens laid their regular quota of eggs. The sun shone, and even Keijo's morose disposition seemed to lighten as the days drifted by, each one so like the other that only by marking off the calendar could we remember which day was which.

Alan used to get up out of his sleeping-bag at 6 A.M. and wrestle with the rusty cross-cut to an accompaniment of unceasing blasphemy.

Jerry and I, waked from sleep by the crashes and shouts of anger on the beach below, would murmur drowsy comments to each other on his abusive and one-sided conversations with God and sink back comfortably to sleep.

At eight o'clock we got up ourselves. Stepping outside the cabin door, we used to draw in deep breaths of balsam-scented air and feast our eyes on beauty as a prelude to the day's work.

By this time the sun was streaming down and the whole world awake and doing, a blue and white world sprayed with gold and filled with exciting sounds. Looking down from the cliff top, we could see the blue, rippled sea covered with speckles of white froth, the tossing masses of plum blossom in Keijo's orchard, white hens with wind-ruffled feathers preening themselves in the shadows of old wind-falls, seagulls wheeling with ecstatic cries over our heads, squirrels frisking up and down the fir branches, a blue heron brooding in a shallow pool, and pouring down over it all like a benison, the warm, golden sun.

Presently, as the more mundane things of life claimed our attention, the stove-pipe joined in the symphony of colour and scent, and aromatic spirals of wood smoke began to rise in the air, the smell of coffee and frying bacon floated through the open door and window, and breakfast was eaten to an accompanying view of mossy rocks and forest trees with glimpses of the shining sea between them, while a fresh, salty wind blew the curtains about.

We kept our little battery radio on a shelf by the window and as we ate, surrounded by all this loveliness, we listened sometimes as if to another world—to European news flashes, uneasy stock-market reports, and harassed statesmen arguing over international politics; and we wondered why people should ever think such things important.

Now and then we would try to find a program more in keeping with our surroundings, but all the music that came out sounded flat and discordant against the magic harmonies of wind and sea.

"I used to like opera once," said Jerry on one occasion, twisting the dials. "I always went to the first nights. But something seems to have happened to all the operatic singers these days. They sound like Arkansas hog callers."

"And I bet you couldn't tell them from the hogs," added Alan, who disliked opera.

"Oh come on now, not *all* of them," I interjected.

Alan put his feet up on the table and tilted his chair back.

"*All* of them. The last Lohengrin I saw looked as if he had been blown up with a bicycle pump."

He took a long pull at his pipe.

"And did you ever see a Brunnhilde that weighed less than three hundred pounds? Every time I hear the fire music played I can see her frying on a steam table like an outsize chop."

Gradually the radio fell into disuse and we found the music of the wind and waves a more satisfactory accompaniment to our daily lives.

From breakfast time on, our outdoor work was continuous with only a brief pause for a sandwich lunch, eaten outside.

After sundown came the main meal of the day, for which we assembled in the "dining-room."

The "dining-room" was a cleared space under the pine trees on the rocky bluff that overlooked the lagoon. The furniture consisted of a wicker table and some canvas chairs. Here we sat and drank our after-dinner tea, the flavour perfumed strangely by the pine needles that fell into it from the green boughs overhead.

With the evening, we rested from our labours, and drifting in lazy content on the lagoon, we gave ourselves up to contemplation of the night. A faintly creaking oarlock would be muffled with an old rag so that no sound should disturb the wonderful stillness, and we steered up the wrinkled path of light shed by a big honey-coloured moon and for the first time in our lives were in complete harmony with our surroundings.

The newspapers sent to us by city friends piled up unread beside the silent radio, and for us the outside world ceased to exist.

Chapter 6

ONE OF the chief disadvantages of life in the wilderness, according to our city friends, was lack of medical services.

"Suppose you are sick?" they had asked.

We had blithely explained that people who pioneer don't ever get sick; the very fact of knowing that there are no doctors handy keeps them well.

"You are either alive or dead, there's no in-between stage," I told them bluntly.

Our listeners shook their heads and continued to visualize us with broken legs and arms, acute appendicitis, ruptures, and all the other ailments which they insisted beset the average wilderness dweller. Then one of them came across an article in a magazine describing the activities of a fleet of hospital ships which, under the auspices of an organization called the "Columbia Coast Mission," plied up and down the coast, visiting isolated settlements, penetrating into places which were out of the track of the coastal steamers, and dispensing a mixture of physical and spiritual comfort to the afflicted.

Death being frequently a sudden and violent affair in these regions, the most important member of the crew was the parson, whose job it was to administer the last rites where possible, console the bereaved, if any, and arrange for the disposal of what was left of a body cut to pieces by a flying cable or crushed beyond recognition by a falling tree.

The report of the fine work done by the hospital ships was offset by the grim description of the conditions under which many of their patients lived, and the graphic and lurid accounts of accidental deaths reduced our friends to a state of despair.

"I can't imagine why you want to go and bury yourselves in a place like that—anything could happen to you."

"Anything could happen to us here," I had retorted. "You take your life in your hand every time you cross the road, and you can get bopped on the head by a thug or trapped in an elevator or trampled to death at a bargain sale—there's simply no end to the different ways of dying in a city."

Our worried friends had ended by imploring us to contact one of the hospital ships at the first possible moment and ask them to check on us occasionally to see if we were still alive.

"I can just see myself doing it," muttered Jerry darkly. "It's bad enough to have casual visitors breathing down your neck every time you have a free day in town, but to deliberately start that kind of thing when all we are trying to do is to get away from it all just doesn't make sense."

We had therefore decided that in the ordinary course of events the chances of our meeting with any of the hospital ships were extremely remote, and it was with considerable astonishment, mixed with some consternation, that we saw, one afternoon, one of them riding at anchor outside the lagoon. The consternation became acute when we noticed preparations being made for a sortie into the lagoon.

Compulsory Sunday-school attendance in our early youth had resulted in our growing up with a shy suspicion of anyone who wore a collar back to front, and as Keijo's fury of hatred for anything remotely connected with religion was only equalled by the utter indifference shown by Joel and his brothers, the astonishment and consternation were general.

It was mail day, and the residents of Quiet Waters were all preparing to race out in a spanking westerly breeze to meet the mail boat. Joel, being in the advantageous position of owning a house that faced towards the entrance of the lagoon and also being the fortunate possessor of a strong pair of field-glasses, was the first to spy the vessel and the preparations for a pastoral visit; and he and his brothers promptly jumped into their fishing boat and, without waiting for full slack, shot the rapids and headed out to sea as if the devil were nipping at their heels.

It was this unusual proceeding that drew our attention to the graceful white ship anchored outside the lagoon.

"Cripes! Visitors!" cried Jerry. "You don't suppose they are coming in to see us, do you? By golly, I believe they are—and it's mail day, too. Come on, let's get out of here, tide's nearly slack."

We untied *Dizzy Lizzy* and rowed with all possible speed to the rapids, shot through the still-swirling waters, and on the other side came face to face with the sea-going parson, who was sitting in his dinghy watching the ominous-looking eddies with interest.

"Too late," groaned Jerry.

The parson smiled and beckoned to us.

"Come on, we can't be rude," I murmured under my breath and pulled slowly up beside him, shipped my oars, gripped the gunwales of his heaving boat and waited.

Introducing himself, he announced his intention of paying a visit to the residents of the lagoon as soon as the rapids had calmed down sufficiently to allow him to bring his dinghy through the entrance.

"I wouldn't try it," I warned, "you might not be able to get back."

"I can wait for the next tide."

"But that's six hours!" I gasped, appalled.

Jerry kicked me and I subsided.

Our boat drifted away while we discussed the situation in low tones.

"He'll be here for tea and we haven't a thing in the house to eat," I said, my mind running anxiously over the contents of the larder. "Of course, we could go out and not come back," I added hopefully.

"We'd have to come back some time," answered Jerry grimly. "Serves you right for not baking that batch of stuff you've been talking about for the last week."

We drifted back, and Jerry, avoiding my outraged look, smiled hospitably at the visitor.

"I'm so sorry, but I have to go and pick up the mail; but Margot here will take you into the lagoon and give you some tea."

I transferred myself to the parson's boat, and casting a look of hate in Jerry's direction, picked up an oar and poled carefully through the eddies and whirlpools until we were once more in the calm waters of the lagoon.

When we reached our own property my eyes fell on the unconscious Alan, stripped to the waist and busily squaring a log with the broad-axe, which he had early informed us was never intended as a tool for chopping kindling.

My frantic pantomime behind the visitor's back, depicting a cleric in the attitude of prayer and the necessity for being decently clad for a meeting with such, brought nothing but an open-mouthed and uncomprehending stare from my relative, and my gyrations were interrupted when the parson turned to me with a grave smile and said, "Please don't. I am quite used to seeing lumberjacks without shirts."

Flushed with mortification, I turned on an embarrassed smile and suggested a tour of the property. During the course of the next hour, the guest was walked up and down the rocky hillside, shown over the half-finished log house, the goat and chicken sheds, formally introduced to all the livestock, and trailed through the swamp to the vegetable garden and the lake. At the end his cheerful freshness contrasted sharply with my exhaustion.

"I hope I haven't tired you," I panted when our tour ended down on the beach.

"Oh no! I am quite used to climbing mountains and walking

through the bush." His even breathing and calm manner made it quite evident to me that he was.

Crossing over towards the log house, the parson picked up the cross-cut saw and looked at it critically.

"Needs setting badly, doesn't it?" he said mildly.

Alan, sweating profusely under the heavy shirt which he had donned as a concession to the church, threw a hostile look in his direction and began an indignant murmuring which I knew to be the prelude to a more profane outburst.

"Come up to the cabin and have some tea," I interposed hastily.

Hurrying ahead, intent on getting our guest out of earshot as quickly as possible, I looked anxiously in the direction of the cabin, remembering the unmade beds and the unwashed dishes.

"I am afraid the place is not very tidy," I apologized as I opened the door. "Today is mail day and we didn't have time to do much to the house."

"Oh, I have been in untidier places than this," said the parson, straightening the covers on one of the camp cots and sitting down. "Sometimes when men have been living alone in the bush for years, they almost forget they are human."

I surreptitiously pushed the rug into place with my foot, snatched up a pink satin brassiere which was dangling over a chair back, and dropped a towel over a roll of toilet-paper which was prominently displayed on the dining table.

"We haven't arrived at that stage yet," I said. "This place is a mess, I know, but when we get the new house built things will be different."

I went outside for a handful of kindling and while I lit the fire and made tea, the parson subjected me to a thorough catechism.

"I suppose the other young lady is your sister? . . . No? Your cousin? . . . A friend! Well, well. . . . And you are building a house? Amazing! I presume you are here for a holiday?"

"No, we are here to live," I said bluntly, as I swept a pile of dirty socks off the table and planted a plate of stale cake there instead.

The parson pursued his theme.

"But my dear young lady, what was your object in coming to a place like this?" And he cast a puzzled glance round the cluttered cabin with all its horrid details of tangled bedclothes and soiled pans.

I looked out of the window at the mountains and sea and thought of the elfin magic of the starlit nights, the croon of the wind in the trees, and the restless music of the waves.

"We like it here."

The parson looked at me with unbelief.

"You *like* it?"

I lapsed into silence and nibbled a piece of dry cake sadly.

"You'll soon get sick of it," he said, summing up the situation. "Just wait till winter comes, you'll be sighing for the comforts of civilization."

I refilled his teacup and juggled some of Alan's less reputable reading matter into a more inconspicuous position.

Conversation turned to the subject of the hospital ships and their duties. While sipping his tea and struggling through a slice of tough cake, the visitor told me the story of the vessels and painted a vivid word picture of the sturdy boats fighting their way through stormy seas on their errands of mercy, in and out of bays and inlets to lonely camps and isolated settlements, bringing news of the outside world to people who had lost touch with it; education and entertainment in the form of moving pictures to children who had no knowledge of anything outside their own forests; caring for the sick, baptizing the newly born, burying the dead, and keeping a watchful patrol of the coast ready to give aid when it was needed.

I looked at him with respect. This demonstration of practical Christianity was a completely new aspect of religion and I tried to make up for former inhospitable thoughts by pressing more tea and dry cake on him.

"No thank you," he said draining his cup and getting up from the bed with difficulty, "but seeing I am here I suppose I had better call on the other residents."

"There are only Joel and his brothers, and they have gone to meet the mail boat." I paused doubtfully, then added: "There's Keijo, of course. He is home today, but he doesn't like church people. He says the Bible was written by the Government to fool people into believing that if they put up with being oppressed by the capitalists in this world, they might get a chance of being capitalists themselves in the next."

A flicker of amusement showed in the parson's eyes.

"I must certainly go and see him."

"Well, be careful. Keijo generally carries a gun and he is an awfully good shot."

I escorted him down to the beach and saw him off. His boat vanished round the point that divided us from Keijo's homestead. I heard his engine stop as he drew in to the wharf and five minutes later we saw him leaving in a hurry, pursued by loud and angry imprecations.

"Looks as if Keijo won that round," said Alan in tones of satisfaction as he watched the dinghy heading for the entrance channel.

"It's too bad he couldn't have stayed long enough to hear Keijo's views on religion. They would have turned his hair grey."

It was not until early evening that the boats returned from their trip out for the mail. First the steady chugging of a heavy-duty engine heralded the approach of Joel's fishing boat, and it swept noisily past, sending a wash up onto the beach and bringing barks of protest from the dogs.

Soon after them came Sundi in a small power boat, her plump body shrouded in a waterproof of shapeless cut and hideous design, and her thick fair hair crowned with a knitted teapot cover.

Last of all, Jerry, pulling manfully at the oars of her skiff and looking hopefully towards the cabin for signs of the smoking stovepipe which indicated that supper was being prepared.

"Why, oh why is Christianity so all-pervading?" said she, poking a cautious face round the door-post and peering suspiciously around.

"It's all right," I assured her, "he's gone home full of stale cake and he probably thinks we live like a bunch of Indians. There were goat droppings on the floor and toilet-paper on the dining table and a line of dirty socks hanging from the rafters. The place looked like a Kaffir kraal."

"What did he expect?" said Jerry, sitting down to her supper. "You don't look for social amenities in the wilds."

I tied a dish-towel over my blue jeans and, lifting the saucepan off the stove, proceeded to ladle out large helpings of curried fish and fried potatoes onto the empty plates, and for a brief moment a different scene flashed across my mind. A room in a quiet stone house in another, older land. A room full of flowers and flickering firelight where a stately white-haired hostess sat behind a lace-covered table and poured China tea into fragile cups. For a moment the long-forgotten taste of watercress sandwiches came back to me. I dropped the spoon into the smoke-blackened pan and stared out of the window at the wild Canadian scenery.

"Damask napkins and Sèvres china," I murmured dreamily, "—we have come a long way from those things."

"That's what I mean," said Jerry, busily stuffing potatoes into her mouth. "The combination of curates and crumpets is an evil that belongs solely to civilization."

The coming of the hospital ship into our uneventful lives proved to be the chief topic of conversation for the next few days, and the Nelson brothers, having escaped the first visitation, lived in a state of wary suspense; but their vigilance relaxed as time went on. The hospital ship never came again and Quiet Waters maintained its heathen state undisturbed.

Meanwhile, as the summer days grew warmer and longer, work on the log house slowed down. A beautiful languor enveloped us and we found lying on the hot, fragrant moss in the sun between frequent dips in the green water of the lagoon much pleasanter than slaving over the house.

There were days when we never touched a tool.

The half-finished house, with its partly raised walls and empty window-frames, stared blindly out to sea while we passed the time revelling in the sun and blissfully inhaling the aromatic scent of pine needles and seaweed.

"I don't think we'll ever get this house built, do you?" I said, looking at the big log which Alan had been lazily poking at for the past week. "Does it matter?" said Jerry idly, "I hate to waste this good weather working. We can live in the cabin just as well."

"You can't leave your furniture standing out in that tent all winter—it'll rot," said Alan, looking up. "Let's see, how much time have we got left?"

An examination of the calendar proved that the end of August was approaching, when Alan would have to return to town; and it was quite evident that the log house would not be finished before he had to leave. Roused out of our dreaming existence, we plunged into the building with belated energy.

"If I can get the walls up, it's all I'll have time to do," said Alan. "You'll just have to finish it yourselves."

For the next two weeks we worked feverishly, cutting logs, peeling, notching, and putting them into place; and finally the walls were complete and ready for the capping-logs.

It took the three of us to roll the first of the two thirty-two-foot capping-logs to the base of the wall, then we sat down and smoked a cigarette while we pondered ways and means of raising it up to the top. After discussing and discarding several methods, we decided to raise one end of the log onto a low trestle. This done, we transferred ourselves to the other end and raised that to an equal level. From this, after a rest and another cigarette, we raised it one end at a time onto higher trestles; and finally with infinite difficulty we all got our shoulders underneath it and tried to ease it to the top of the wall. During the raising process, I stepped out from under my end, while Jerry walked into a hole in the floor and disappeared into the foundations, leaving Alan reeling under the full weight of the log.

The sulphurous volley of language issuing from the hole in the floor, coupled with the bloodcurdling yells of Alan, sent me scurrying headlong for help. I returned with the triumphantly grinning Keijo, whose grudging assistance made the task of capping the walls a little less hazardous.

More lumber for the floors and window-frames had to be sent for from the city. It arrived by mail steamer in a violent storm and as none of the boats were big enough to hold it, the planks had to be tossed overboard into the sea; and before they could be collected, the waves had broken the ropes that bound them and washed them away down the coast-line.

"Yoicks! Tallyho!"

I dug my oars into the water and, rising up on the crest of a big wave, shouted to the others.

"Come on you guys, give us a hand here."

Before the eyes of the astounded passengers, the islanders' boats nosed into the waves like a pack of hunting dogs and scattered in chase of the bobbing lumber.

Bit by bit it was retrieved and collected together, and while the mail was being sorted, Magnus and Big Pete tied it together and anchored it off one of the islands until the storm should calm down sufficiently to allow us to tow it into the lagoon. After that, the wet, seaweedy boards had to be carried up from the shore, one at a time, and stacked to dry out in the sun before they could be used. Then the back-breaking work of building commenced again.

Sometimes the days were so hot that we worked in our bathing-suits and were driven to the point of desperation by the onslaughts of deer flies and other carnivorous insects, which settled on our bare skin in clouds and took triangular bites out of us. When stung beyond endurance, we dived into the sea, swam round until the burning had gone out of the bites, and came out dripping to resume work. Even Keijo could find no fault with the way we worked now. It was a steady grind from sunrise to dusk. We lost a lot of weight and grew lean and brown and hard. Muscles appeared in places which previously had been soft and flabby, and heavy weights which we used to think were beyond our strength became surprisingly light.

"I never felt so well or happy in all my life," I used to say frequently with a sort of surprise. "I don't know why people don't take to the wilds *en masse*. I'll never, never go back to a city again."

We had no set hours for anything. Our day of physical labour ended when the sun went down. Supper was eaten out of doors under the trees; then—deck chairs, cigarettes and complete relaxation as, in silence, we watched the mountains opposite slowly change colour and cast pansy-purple shadows on the lagoon. An occasional flock of wild ducks flew home in the sunset, their wings whistling in the warm still air. The summer moon rose slowly over the tops of the trees and shone down on the sleeping lagoon; a loon's haunted cry was heard in the distance and then the silence fell, enveloping everything. Stretching luxuriously, we rose from our chairs and with a murmured good-night went to our hard cots and a deep, dreamless sleep.

At last came the day when Alan had to return to civilization, and it was with many and loud laments that he looked his last on the half-finished house, the sparkling lagoon and the blue mountains.

"If I can get away from that damn job of mine, I'll be up later," he promised; "but with the time I've been away already I'm likely to find no job at all when I get back." His eyes lit up for a moment. "In that case I'll be back right away. Gee, I sure hate to leave this place."

Jerry and I went down to the beach to bale out the boat while he packed his rucksack and rolled up his sleeping-bag. As was usual, there was a complete lack of coincidence between slack tide and steamer time. In order not to miss the few minutes when the rapids were slack, we took our lunch and, rowing down the lagoon, tied the boat to a rock, climbed up the cliffs overlooking the rapids and settled down to eat and wait for the propitious moment when it was safe to float through.

As we waited, the rising tide filled the channel. The thunderous roar echoing between the canyon walls died away and was followed by the sudden calm which came with slack water.

Jerry and Alan hurriedly piloted the boat through the channel while I remained behind on the cliff top and watched them go, rising and falling on the waves until they vanished round a rocky cape; then I stretched myself out on the soft, thick moss and slept in the sun.

The sun had dipped behind the hills before Jerry returned, weary and drenched with sea water. The steamer had been on time, but the necessity of waiting for the low slack had kept her outside for a period of six hours.

We rowed home, missing Alan's salty chatter and lively spirits. It was the end of August and the evenings were beginning to draw in. As we stepped ashore we looked in silence at the house and the mess surrounding it—unsightly tree stumps, raggedly hacked by the blunt axes; piles of branches stacked for burning; chips of wood littered all over the moss; and in the middle of it all, our dream house—roofless, windowless, and doorless, with a great gaping hole where the fireplace was to be and the cold night wind whistling through the open foundations.

"Oh," I groaned, "how hopeless it all looks! We have one month's fine weather left to finish this ancient Roman ruin. I really don't see how it is going to be done."

"We'll manage it," said Jerry with cheerful optimism as we climbed the hill to the cabin. "Let's have supper and a good night's rest and tomorrow we will think about the house."

While Jerry lit the fire and filled the oil lamps, I prepared supper and switched on the neglected radio set, and as we ate our corned-beef hash and fried potatoes we listened with complete detachment to the latest thing in international crises.

"They're still at it," I said; and thinking of Alan I added, "Fancy going back to *that*!"

Next morning we woke bright and early to wrestle anew with the problem of getting the house finished in a month's time.

First we paid a visit to Keijo. He was not encouraging.

"You no building house. It falling down," he said when confronted with our building problems. "Only *men* can building houses."

"There is no law against women building them is there?" said Jerry angrily.

To this remark, Keijo merely presented an aloof silence; and realizing that we could expect no help from him, we rowed away.

Next, we visited the Nelsons, who received our problems sympathetically; and seated round the oilcloth-covered table in their substantial home, we listened to their advice.

"You've made a good start on it," said Blackie. "There's no reason why you shouldn't finish it in a month."

"If we could only get a roof on the darn thing," I said, "I believe we could manage all right. How do you go about putting a roof on?"

"You must make the roof of cedar shakes," said Joel.

"What's a cedar shake?" asked Jerry anxiously.

"We-e-el," replied Joel, rolling a cigarette and pushing the tobacco tin across the table towards us, "it's like a big shingle"; and he proceeded to explain the process of sawing three-foot lengths off large cedar logs, splitting the piece into four lengthwise, and then with a heavy metal blade called a frow, slicing off thin layers of wood.

"Jumping Joseph!" exclaimed Jerry in dismay, "I never heard of such a thing. What do we nail them to?"

"The sheeting, of course."

"What's sheeting?" I queried.

"The boards that run across the rafters."

"But we haven't got any rafters," I said helplessly, "all we have is four walls. I guess we'll just have to use that tarpaulin."

Joel suppressed a smile and said quietly, "I guess we can put up the rafters for you."

Next day, Joel and 'Lias arrived early in the morning, inspected our battered tools, shook their heads and went back for their own. By night the ridge-pole was up and all the rafters in place.

We looked admiringly up at the gaunt skeleton outlined against the sky.

"Why, it really looks like a house now," I said.

"We'll be round tomorrow to nail on the sheeting," said 'Lias, picking up his jacket.

"Oh no," said Jerry in a sudden outburst of independence, "you have done enough for us. We can manage the rest ourselves."

The men looked doubtfully at us and then up at the steeply pitched roof.

"You don't aim to climb up there yourselves, do you?" Joel asked.

"Of course—there's nothing to it," said Jerry stoutly.

I quaked inwardly but kept silent.

"Well—" 'Lias and Joel shrugged, picked up their tools and with a sideways glance from us to the roof again, strolled with their usual slow, easy stride to their boat.

After they had gone, we looked at each other.

"Well?" I challenged.

"Well," retorted Jerry, "I don't know whether we can or not, but I wasn't going to let them think we couldn't."

The next few days were spent in a feverish search for cedar out of which to make shakes for the roof.

Old windfalls, scarred by forest fires, were dug out of the mossy undergrowth, sawn into three-foot lengths with the rusty cross-cut, and split into quarters with the sledge-hammer and wedges. Then Jerry held the frow in place and I swung a heavy wooden club down on the blade, and one by one the sheets of cedar split off and fell to the ground.

"This is fun," said Jerry. "I could do this all day."

Future developments proved that it was not to be such fun. The island had been thoroughly logged of all its best timber in earlier days, and the few logs of clear cedar which were necessary for our shakes were scarce or else in inaccessible places. Sometimes in our search we would come across what we thought was a piece of clear cedar only to find on sawing it through that it was full of knots or had a bad cross-grain which prevented it from splitting into the shakes we needed so badly.

The end of the first week found us with barely a handful of shakes fit to use.

"No cedar here," said Keijo, "cedar way back, way back in swamp," and he made a wide sweep with his arm.

"How do you get it out?" inquired Jerry.

"Cut shakes in swamp; carry out on back—two or three miles maybe," replied Keijo, who believed nothing that was done was any good unless accompanied by the maximum amount of effort.

"Oh yeah!" jeered Jerry.

"Two or three miles!" I murmured, appalled. "Say, to the devil with this house! How about digging a hole in the ground and putting up an umbrella?"

But Keijo did not understand such levity, and he went off muttering "Cedar way back, way back," and we resumed our search.

The shakes when split were so heavy that we could carry only about eight at a time down to the house. As we wandered ever further into the forest in our continuous hunt for cedar, leaving behind us little piles of broken and discarded shakes and half-sawn logs, we found it harder and harder to struggle through the bush with its tangled undergrowth; so we decided to vary the monotony of the work by nailing the sheeting onto the rafters and covering it with the shakes which we had already collected.

The ladder was propped up against the house, and the boards hauled painfully up onto the roof and nailed to the rafters. As the sheeting came nearer to the peak, difficulties increased. I soon found out that I was a victim of that mysterious phobia that attacks people who venture aloft, and my efforts to scramble up the sides of the steeply pitched roof holding the end of a board generally ended in a panic-stricken and head-swimming form of hysteria as I let go of my end and sprawled crablike, frantically searching for footholds which were not there.

Keijo, rowing past one day when we were thus occupied, and taking in my inefficiency with grim satisfaction, shouted:

"Huh—you never getting roof on."

"We will," I shouted back, digging my nails into the cracks between the boards and risking one eye in a quick glance over my shoulder.

"Ha, ha!" came back in accents of scorn. "You not putting roof on—you falling off."

"Maybe I will fall off," I shouted back in anger from the roof where I was spread out like a starfish, "but the roof will be put on first."

The handful of shakes we had collected seemed pitifully small when we nailed them on.

"They don't seem to go anywhere, do they?" I said despairingly to Joel, who had come over to see how we were progressing with the roof.

"Reckon you'll need about two thousand," answered Joel thoughtfully. "That's a mighty big roof."

"If only cedar wasn't so scarce," moaned Jerry. "It's not as if we could cut down fresh trees. It has to be old and seasoned."

Our searching continued and each day added a few more shakes to the pile we were stacking outside the house. Each piece of cedar that we found was an occasion of loud rejoicing. Still we seemed to need more shakes and still more shakes. In our desperation we even made excursions into the swamps "way back," but there was no cedar or else we did not look in the right places for it. All we found was a nest of angry hornets who expressed their resentment in the usual manner of hornets, and we retired in haste and disorder pursued by a zooming cloud of furious insects. The rest of that day was spent in anointing ourselves with ammonia.

Next, we subjected the piles of discarded shakes to a second scrutiny and picked out some that in our first enthusiasm we had rejected.

At last we managed to cover half the roof but already the weather was breaking and showers of rain had fallen.

We took down the tent, stored the furniture in the completed portion of the house and draped the now sodden canvas from the rafters to shut off the unfinished part and prevent the rain from driving in. With dogged determination we forced ourselves back into the damp, gloomy forest every morning with our frow and club and recommenced our search for cedar, and little by little the second half of the roof began to sprout rows of three-foot shakes.

One evening, utterly weary, we were mechanically splitting off the shakes, our minds more occupied with thoughts of supper than with what we were doing, when I accidentally brought the wooden club down with all my strength on Jerry's hand.

For one horrified moment we both stared speechless at the flattened fingers; and visions of myself rowing frantically about on the sea looking for the hospital ship, while Jerry bled to death in the forest, raced through my mind. Then Jerry lifted the injured hand to her mouth and rushed back to the cabin roaring with anguish while I stumbled after her saying idiotically, "Gee I'm sorry, I didn't mean to."

Back in the cabin, Jerry collapsed on the bed and I busied myself boiling water and getting bandages out of the first-aid kit. On examination I found the injured hand had the skin broken in several places and one finger was completely flattened and so discoloured that it looked like a piece of raw hamburger.

"I think it's broken," moaned Jerry. "I feel sick. God, if I only had a drink!"

"God, I wish we had," was my heartfelt reply, "I feel sick too."

All we could raise in the way of remedies was hot water with Epsom salts in it, and in this solution we soaked the injured hand and bound the worst-looking finger up in splints made out of bits of kindling.

For the next two or three days the mere idea of returning to the woods made us shudder; but at last, the broken finger showing no sign of disintegration, the urgency of our task drove us back to the now loathsome business of shake cutting. We found our tools lying on the ground just as we had left them. Reluctantly we picked up the club and the frow and resumed work, with more care.

"For Pete's sake, when you write home next, don't tell anybody," I begged. "I hate to have them say 'I told you so.'"

The bare spaces on the roof gradually grew less and one day there was only a quarter left to cover; then an eighth; then one morning Jerry said, "I think one more day will finish it."

Next day, with breath-taking relief, we saw the last of the two thousand shakes nailed on.

"The roof's on! The roof's on!" we shouted, capering ecstatically about in the strangely darkened interior.

The last touch, in the shape of a double layer of shiplap on the peak of the roof, was still needed. As the idea of sawing the shiplap into lengths easy to handle never occurred to us, the next morning saw us crawling up the side of the roof, each of us hanging onto the end of an eighteen-foot length of shiplap and shivering with fright as we looked over our shoulders at the sharp rocks below and the greedy waves licking at them.

"By golly, once I've got this roof on, I'll never take my feet off the ground again as long as I live," babbled Jerry with chattering teeth.

When the last nail had been driven in and both of us were safely back on earth again, we surveyed our work with pride and solemnly shook hands.

Keijo, rowing past, as he frequently did these days, paused and looked with cold eyes at our efforts.

"First snow come—roof falling in," he commented briefly, and rowed on.

"Don't take any notice of him," said 'Lias, who had come over to inspect our work. "You have made a good job of it." He ran his tongue over his cigarette paper and repeated slowly as he looked up at the rows of shakes, "A very good job."

Our spirits, dashed by Keijo's criticism, rose again.

There was still more to be done. First, the windows had to be put in place.

The smaller windows in the kitchen slid easily into the sockets which Alan had made for them, but the big-view windows in the living-room were not so easily managed. These were each composed of three panes of glass, each pane measuring three feet by five. The centre pane was intended to be a sliding affair which could open

Our dream house—roofless,
windowless, and doorless . . .

"Oh," I groaned, "how hopeless
it all looks!"

I sallied forth with a light heart . . .
to construct a privy.

This time our task was really finished and the house complete.

The centre pane actually did open and shut!

Going out to meet the mail steamer.

and shut. Nobody was more surprised than we were when we found, on completing the job, that the centre pane actually *did* open and shut.

"What do you know about that?" exclaimed Jerry in surprise. "It works!"

Then came the doors.

One door we had bought ready-made, but when the time came for it to be hung, we found a decided discrepancy between it and the space which Alan had left for it.

"The door is too big," said Jerry in worried tones; "we will have to saw some off."

Owing to some mistake in calculation, the door after the sawing operation turned out to be too small.

"We'll have to fill in the frame somehow," said Jerry, sounding still more worried. "We can't put the piece back on the door."

With endless difficulty and much bickering, the doorway was filled in at the top and the door once more placed in the opening.

"It's too big," said Jerry with ominous patience.

"Saw some more off," I said blithely, "we'll never get all that filling out of the doorway."

Half an hour later the door was too small again and Jerry was almost weeping with exasperation.

"If we go on like this we won't have any door left; the opening looks like the entrance to a blasted igloo already."

"Never mind," I consoled her, "we can always go in and out of the front door and keep the back one for Suey."

The front door was a magnificent affair made of boards, strengthened with heavy cross-beams. It had large metal hinges and ornamental studding made out of old bottle caps; and more by good luck than good management, it fitted the door frame.

"Boy, we're really getting good," I said with enthusiasm.

As a finishing touch we screwed a brass knocker to the outside of the door and used it scrupulously every time we let ourselves in.

We made a little porch with the scraps of left-over lumber and four steps leading from it to the ground, and once again we had to take time off for admiration. Then we laid building paper over the floor and nailed down another layer of flooring. We reinforced the arched roof with extra supports made of curved cedar roots, stripped of their bark and polished to a dull bronze.

There still remained the fireplace.

For this we brought buckets of sand from a sand-bar on the other side of the lagoon, rowing miles back and forth in our flat-bottomed boat. We mixed the sand with the cement which we had brought up with us; rolled rocks down the hillside and built them up for a hearth, anchoring them with concrete; then, with the cold weather practically upon us and knowing that we would not have time to construct a chimney, we boarded in the back and sent to town for a big air-tight heater.

"We can finish the chimney next summer," said Jerry. "After all, we have all our lives before us to do it."

The arranging of the furniture in the thirty-foot living-room came next. The gracious proportions of the room with its high arched ceiling lent themselves generously to the handsome articles of furniture which we had brought with us. Carpets were laid. Curtains were hung at the big windows. Bookshelves to hold our three hundred books were built. Chairs and coffee-tables and lamps found their own appropriate niches. The chesterfield was placed by the hearth and cushions blossomed out of the depths of armchairs. Mirrors and tapestries appeared on the walls. A hand-carved Dutch cabinet full of silver ornamented one wall and a gate-legged table holding antique copper candlesticks and a Russian samovar adorned another. Linoleum was laid on the kitchen floor and cupboards were built. The tea-chests which had held our china were unpacked and transformed into flour and sugar bins. The camp cots with their chintz covers were placed in an alcove; and last of all, we took apart the stove-pipes and hauled the iron camp cooker down the hill from the cabin to the new house on the shore.

Putting the pipes together again and sawing a hole in the wall for them to go through was another story and one which haunted our dreams for weeks after; but when it was completed, the stove-pipes miraculously fitted the opening and we jubilantly lit a blazing fire.

Keijo, rowing curiously around and seeing the smoke rise, hurried ashore, utterly unable to believe his eyes. He looked round the house with an expressionless face; then, producing a bottle of home-made wine from the pocket of his oilskin jacket, he said:

"In my country . . . we having custom . . . drink good luck to first fire."

So we drank good luck to the first fire. Keijo, although no power on earth could ever have induced him to admit that the house was a success, at least on this occasion managed to refrain from adverse criticism; and as we drank the wine, he thawed out considerably. When his stern features relaxed, he became what nature had originally intended him to be—a handsome man.

Our joy in our new home was short-lived, because with nightfall came a cold wind that blew through the cracks in the shakes, stirred the hair on our heads, and caused the lamp wicks to flare and the stove to puff out large clouds of choking white smoke.

We huddled round the stove wrapped in our warmest coats and listened to the wind whistling round the rafters, and our spirits fell to zero.

"And this is only September," said Jerry. "What do you suppose it will be like by Christmas?"

At bedtime we piled all the available blankets on the beds and lay shivering, unable to sleep. When the fire in the stove smouldered out, the cold was so intense that we both crowded into one cot for warmth and suffered all the discomforts of sardines in a can for the remainder of the night.

Next day another council of war was held. Keijo was called in for advice.

"You getting plenty of heat when roof lined," said he, hardly able to conceal his glee at the unfortunate turn of events; but he offered no suggestions as to how we were to line it, or what we were to line it with.

"False beams and shakes," said Joel.

"You mean we have to go through all that splitting and sawing and clubbing and hunting for cedar again?" I asked in despair.

"Reckon so if you don't want to freeze to death this winter," replied Joel.

With inward groans we recommenced the weary business of shake cutting.

"D'you remember once you said this was fun?" I reminded Jerry.

The lining of the roof took us a long time, and at nights we continued to suffer from the cold until we hit on the happy expedient of heating rocks in the oven, wrapping them in paper, and scattering them about the beds. We nestled down among them and woke in the morning with rocky patterns all over us; but the rocks retained their heat all night and in the daytime we were so busy working that we did not have time to notice the cold.

As we filled in the cathedral-like arch of the roof, we stuffed the space between it and the lining with old newspapers and magazines, sacks full of moss scraped from the rocks, and anything we could find that would serve as insulation.

The chinks in the logs were plugged with dried moss, shoved in with a sharp stick; and then the heater arrived and we found that our building had become transformed from a draughty barn to a comfortable home. This time our task was really finished and the house complete.

Nothing that we have ever done before or since has ever given us such satisfaction. Every time we came into it, we paused to beam delightedly around and exchange comments on its beauties.

"It's our home," said Jerry proudly, "we made it."

Possibly in those last three words lay its chief charm.

Chapter 7

Now THAT the house was finished we prepared to lapse once more into our former state of happy idleness, and this brought down a storm of protest from Keijo.

"Winter coming. You no have canning vegetables. You no have canning fish. You no have putting eggs in water-glass. You no have doing nothing."

"What the heck is water-glass?" I asked after Keijo and his storm had passed on.

Jerry thumbed through the pages of our encyclopedia of general knowledge.

"It's a kind of preservative. Keeps your surplus eggs fresh so that in the winter when the hens stop laying you won't go short of eggs. I didn't know hens stopped laying in the winter. I thought they just went on and on."

"So did I; and anyway we haven't got any surplus eggs, and if we had we haven't any water-glass to put them in—so that's *that*."

A tour of inspection round the vegetable garden proved that there was nothing left worth canning.

"I guess we didn't plant enough," said Jerry thoughtfully.

"And every time we catch a fish we eat it," I added, "so we can't do anything about it can we?"

Our plans for productive livestock had gone hopelessly awry earlier in the year, when we had found ourselves forced to study the facts of life in order to keep pace with the animals, who in spite of apparent immaturity seemed to be far ahead of us in knowledge.

The first to become afflicted with parental instincts were the hens.

Being totally ignorant of the ways of domestic fowl, we were quite unprepared for the general onset of broodiness which appeared among the flock. Joel, called in to diagnose the case of one old biddy who had appropriated the favourite nesting-box and refused to be dislodged from it, cast a knowing eye over the birds; then, putting his hand into the nest, he brought out an angry heap of feathers and indignant croaks, dropped it on the floor and said:

"She's a clucker."

"All hens cluck," I said, mystified.

"Yes, but this one wants to sit."

"For heaven's sake, she's been sitting for a week," said Jerry in a temper. "I want her to lay eggs."

"Reckon she won't be laying any eggs yet awhile," said Joel, and he patiently explained that the time had come for us to put a clutch of eggs beneath the hen and allow her to hatch out some new chicks. "Then you can start killing off some of the old ones," he ended.

"Good!" I said in a tone of deep satisfaction. "We'll start with that old beast of a rooster."

The rooster had arrived with the hens, thrown in as a goodwill gesture, and his lust and savagery had gained for him the hate and respect of every living thing around.

The hens fled under the chicken house when they saw him approaching; the dogs ran before his onslaughts with anguished yelps, and even the redoubtable Fanny had given him a wide berth.

Jerry and I had both regarded him with terror from the first day when we had gone into the chicken house to collect the eggs and had been violently assaulted by a red-eyed feathered fury whose spurred feet had fallen just short of my face and driven deep into a bare shoulder.

128

"If we have some more chickens there are bound to be roosters among them and we won't need this one," I said. "Let's kill him now."

Once the setting of eggs had been collected and the broody hen left in darkness and solitude to hatch out her family, Jerry and I turned our attention to the disposal of the rooster.

Neither of us had ever killed a chicken, but with our appetites whetted by the prospect of a dinner of roast fowl, we galloped up to the chicken yard full of enthusiasm and murderous intentions.

First the rooster had to be caught.

At the first indication of anything so unusual the whole flock fell into a state of complete hysteria and the rooster took refuge under the hen house.

"You silly beasts," raged Jerry at the fluttering, screeching hens, "can't you see that we're only trying to make happy widows out of you?" She picked up a stone and aimed it under the house, sending the squawking rooster flying out the other side.

A concerted rush on our part cornered the loudly protesting victim in a clump of salal bush and Jerry hauled it out by the leg.

"Now what do we do?" said she, losing some of her enthusiasm.

"Wring its neck," I said promptly.

"You do it."

"I don't know how."

"Neither do I."

We stroked the rooster, our appetite for roast chicken dwindling rapidly.

"Perhaps you could chop off its head?" I suggested tentatively.

"Oh no, I couldn't. It might hurt it."

"Well," I said, at last losing patience, "unless you are going to sit here until it dies a natural death, you had better do *something*."

Jerry sighed.

"I wish Joel was here."

"Well, he isn't."

"Perhaps you could go and get Keijo."

"Keijo thinks we are a couple of bleeding idiots as it is. This

129

would just about finish him. Chop its head off, it won't take a minute."

Jerry sighed again.

"Give me the axe," she said.

I picked up the axe and tested the edge with a cautious thumb and we looked helplessly at each other.

"You do it," pleaded Jerry.

"I can't. You do it," I replied.

Jerry looked round, stalling for time.

"I need a block to lay it on," she said.

I rolled up a block of decayed alder, spongy with age and damp.

"Hold its legs," said Jerry, laying the squirming heap of feathers on the block. "Now hand me the axe."

Hampered by the flapping wings and rearing head, Jerry missed the mark completely with her first blow.

"You'll have to hold its head down too," she said, "how can I chop it off when it's flapping around like that?"

With the next attempt, a shower of spray flew up from the water-logged block and the axe blade sank deep into the soft wood, carrying the rooster with it. We stared a minute in horror at the chunk of wood with a rooster's body sticking out from one side and a startled-looking rooster's head protruding from the other, and then fled in dismay from the scene.

"Where do you suppose the neck went?" murmured Jerry, coming to rest at the foot of a giant fir and leaning against it, exhausted.

I dropped to the moss at her feet.

"I guess it's somewhere in the block." I stirred uneasily and added, "We'll have to go back, it might not be dead."

Creeping stealthily through the wood to the scene of the crime, we peered round the corner of the chicken house fearfully. Everything was just as we had left it. The rooster's head still looked out from the side of the block, eyes open in a shocked, frozen stare.

"It's dead all right," said Jerry, timidly detaching the body and throwing the head into the bush. "Now let's pluck it."

Sitting knee to knee with the headless bird spread over our laps we commenced tearing out the feathers and scattering them over the ground. When we had finished we found that most of the skin had come off with the feathers so that the bird appeared to be not only plucked, but flayed.

We propped the naked corpse on a bench outside the hen house, where it lolled shamelessly, its scaly white legs stuck out at right angles to each other, and its headless neck collapsed on its shoulder.

"I never saw a store chicken look like that," said Jerry in worried tones.

"I know," I replied, "they all have their legs drawn up as though they had stomach-ache."

"Maybe I'd better bend them a bit before *rigor mortis* sets in, and besides we have to clean it, you know."

"*Clean* it?"

"Yes—take out its guts and stuff."

The lesson I received in anatomy during the next half hour completely destroyed my appetite for roast chicken.

"Oy—let's just have poached eggs!" I exclaimed, looking at the debris with a wry face.

Jerry poked curiously about among the grim wreckage.

"Gee, the things you have in your insides! I never realized what a lot of spare parts a person has."

"Stop messing about," I exploded furiously. "Let's get busy and roast the beastly thing."

With a slight return of our former enthusiasm, we heated the oven and roasted the rooster; but as is usually the case, realization did not equal anticipation. After futile attempts to bite into the stringy flesh, Jerry took her drumstick out to the work-bench and attacked it with the bucksaw, while I turned over the pieces of white india-rubber which had been cut off the breast, in a vain search for something tender enough to eat.

"It tastes like stewed boot," said Jerry, glowering at the carcass. "We must have done something wrong, but I can't imagine what it was."

Keijo, hearing of the episode afterwards, looked at us with pitying contempt.

"You should always hanging meat. Two—three days before you are eating," he said.

Joel and 'Lias gave it as their opinion that it was no use trying to roast an old bird and that it would have been better if we had "boiled the bastard."

"After this," said Jerry firmly, "there will be no more chicken dinners. As far as I am concerned, the rest of the hens can die of old age."

Soon after this event, we found ourselves with another problem on our hands. Terrible, the young billy-goat, developing ideas far in advance of his age, sent us weary and worried to searching our encyclopedia for information concerning the age of consent in goats.

The book insisted that a billy-goat should either be kept apart from the herd or else castrated, otherwise unmentionable horrors would result, one of the least being that the milk would "develop an odour."

"That's a polite way of saying it stinks," I said to Jerry. "I always said it did, but as we are not getting any milk, we don't have to worry about *that*."

Jerry looked out of the window at the goats chewing happily away at the raspberry canes.

"I suppose we should keep him in a corral," she said, "but it seems a pity to separate them."

I mentally reviewed the whole co-educational system as applied to goats, and diffidently brought up the alternative measure—castration.

Jerry gave me a startled look and reached unwillingly for the book.

Much searching through the volume did not get us very far. Apart from some awesome illustrations of the tools required for the deed, the information was vague, the author confining himself to the question of the best age and so forth, and in general being decidedly coy about the whole business.

132

"It's no use," said Jerry, throwing the book aside, "unless you want to go it blind with the bread knife, we had better forget the whole business and start building a corral right now."

So for several days we toiled, constructing a corral for Terrible to live in and a little shed to shelter him.

Barely had we completed the task than we found ourselves faced with still another problem; Horrible, the doe, developed dysentery, possibly the result of a too steady diet of raspberry canes.

Horrible at the best of times had a peculiarly offensive odour. Horrible with dysentery perfumed the whole neighbourhood.

"Christ!" said Blackie, coming ashore one day, "what's the matter with that damn goat?"

"She's got trouble with her digestive organs," said Jerry primly.

Blackie gave her a sideways look.

"You'd better do something about it. I got trouble with mine just rowing past the place."

The book was consulted again and a remedy sought for dysentery among goats. It was very clear on this point. Epsom salts, it said.

A check of the first-aid kit revealed nothing more useful that a roll of gauze bandaging, three aspirins, and a bottle of iodine.

My hopeful suggestions regarding the iodine as a solution to the whole problem brought irritated head-shakings from Jerry, and I was instructed to go to Keijo and ask him for some Epsom salts.

I ran Keijo to ground in his kitchen, struggling with his accounts and a lunch of rice pudding, pickles and salt herring.

I stated the case. We needed Epsom salts. Horrible had dysentery.

Keijo looked at me blankly, his mouth full of herring. Here was a word that did not exist in his limited English vocabulary.

I tried again.

"Diarrhoea," I said.

Another uncomprehending stare, accompanied by slow mastication.

"Dear God," I said, clutching my forehead, "just give me some Epsom salts!"

133

Keijo lumbered to his feet, took a brown-paper bag out of a cupboard and handed it to me with a disapproving look.

"You should eating the right food; you no needing Epsom salts," he said.

I seized the bag and retired in disorder, taking a short-cut through Keijo's turnips in my confusion.

The lethal dose of salts which we administered to Horrible removed all signs of dysentery and almost removed Horrible. By the time we had nursed her back to health, the billy-goat had kicked his way out of the corral and sex had reared its ugly head among the dogs. We were treated to the interesting spectacle of a chaste canine nymph vigorously defending her virtue against a horde of doggy satyrs.

"What are we supposed to do," I asked, "give three cheers, or go to her help? We said we wanted to breed dogs; but after all, what do we know about dog breeding?"

"You don't have to know anything," retorted Jerry grimly, "apparently all you have to do is to have dogs."

For several days the animals' love life kept the place in a constant turmoil. Then my repeated rescuings of Suey from the bottom of a pile of furry bodies and Jerry's optimistic prophesies regarding the fine litter of spaniel pups we could expect were finally ended by the action of the bride herself, who turned on her purebred suitors, reduced them to a pulp and then disappeared into the forest, from which she emerged twenty-four hours later with a large police dog trotting at her heels and "fallen woman" written large all over her.

"Well, that's torn it," ejaculated Jerry, surveying her recreant pet with wrathful eyes. "With all those expensive spaniels to choose from, she picks a mangy beast like that!"

Inquiries made afterward proved that the police dog had come to the island with a party of hunters, and wandering in search of adventure had found it on our property and to our cost.

"No spaniel pups now," groaned Jerry. "If she has any at all, they will be a bunch of ugly mongrels of no use to anyone."

We went about our business for the next day or two in a state of gloom, until Keijo, informed of the late event, told us that the possibility of any progeny resulting from such a misalliance was extremely unlikely. His critical eye roving over Horrible's shrunken and twisted body, he added that in his opinion there was no necessity for keeping the billy in a corral.

"Well! That's *that!*" said I, after watching Keijo, scorn exuding from every pore, row away. "As long as the sitting hen doesn't hatch out a crop of two-headed chicks, we don't have to worry."

In due course the rooster's progeny began to make their appearance, and Jerry and I spent the day rushing backwards and forwards between the house and the chicken coop, pacing the floor in the approved fashion, and generally showing a good deal more agitation than the hen.

On our knees before the coop, we were rewarded occasionally by a fascinating glimpse of a tiny yellow head peeping inquisitively out from beneath the old hen's feathers.

"That's four—five—six . . ." gasped Jerry, braving the mother's angry pecks as she pushed a cautious hand beneath her.

Two eggs were found to be in a half-hatched state, the chicken inside appearing to have insufficient strength to finish the job. Anxious to help nature, we peeled off some more of the egg shell and succeeded in extracting two moribund and hideous morsels from the wreckage.

"Look! They're breathing!" shouted Jerry, wild with excitement at the success of her experiment in Caesarian section. "Let's take them down to the house and put them in the oven to dry out."

The chickens were packed into a cardboard box and placed in the oven, and the fire was banked. That done, we hurried back to gloat over the tufts of yellow down that were running about on tiny legs in such an amazing fashion.

By evening the two patients in the oven had dried out sufficiently to be returned to the parental nest, and we went back to the house in a state of jubilation.

"Think of it," exulted Jerry, "twelve eggs—twelve chickens! Not a dud among the lot. I should think that must be some sort of a record."

In a few days the chickens grew their first feathers and in a short time began to look amazingly mature.

"They should start to lay any time now," said Jerry proudly. "Just look at the combs and tails!"

"They not laying before spring," said Keijo when consulted on the matter.

"But they are so big," persisted Jerry.

"They not laying before spring," returned Keijo inexorably.

"Well, come and see for yourself," urged Jerry. "One of them crowed yesterday."

Keijo looked at us with a peculiar expression and walked thoughtfully up to the chicken house.

"There," said Jerry pointing to the twelve rangy objects pecking about in the enclosure, "*now* do you mean to tell me they won't lay before spring?"

Keijo looked at them incredulously.

"They not laying before spring; they not laying ever. They all cocks!"

Keijo was right. All but three of the chickens had turned out to be cocks, and with the collapse of our plans for raising a new crop of hens went all our hopes of eggs for the following season. Furthermore, we found that we had a collection of ravenous young birds to feed.

"We'll be ruined, simply ruined," cried Jerry, wringing her hands. "All they do is eat and eat and eat."

"What do you want with nine roosters?" asked 'Lias, surveying the leggy young inmates of the cock pen. "They are right for frying now."

As Jerry still firmly adhered to her resolution not to kill another hen, a bargain was struck with the strong-and-silent men. They were to kill the roosters; we were to cook them, after which we were all to combine in a fried-chicken debauch.

On the day set for the mass slaughter, Jerry and I betook ourselves into the woods as far as possible to escape from the sound of execution. On our return we found the chickens skinned, cleaned and halved, and looking so utterly unlike the lively, crowing, pecking creatures that we had left, that we could hardly believe the evidence of our eyes.

"There you are. All done," said Joel, rolling down his sleeves.

"Right. Dinner is at one sharp," said Jerry, picking up a skillet and preparing for action.

'Lias and Joel took themselves off home to wash away the traces of murder while I busied myself setting the table, peeling potatoes and preparing salad. Large platters of home-made bread were cut and a dessert concocted of several cans of peaches covered with a topping of marshmallows, beaten egg white and coconut.

"Where will you find anything better than that?" I said proudly, lifting it out of the oven, crisp and delicately browned.

"How are the vegetables? It's ten to one and these chickens are about ready."

"All done," I said, poking at the contents of the pans with a fork. "Just in time—here come the boys."

The four brothers filed in, sniffing the air appreciatively.

"Buggerall! I'm hungry," said Blackie bluntly.

"Sit down, sit down," said I, pulling out chairs and bustling about the table in my best hostess manner.

The men seated themselves at the table and looked inquisitively at the white cloth, the silverware and the glasses.

Sonny lifted up the edge of the tablecloth and examined it with interest, then turning his attention to the forks and spoons, picked them up one by one and looked at the monogram on the handle curiously. A shake of the head and a warning frown from Joel caused him to drop a fork on the floor, and in reaching down for it, he overturned a glass of water, which ran all over the table and soaked the cloth.

His older brothers fixed him with a stony stare while I hastened to remove the cloth and mop up the water from the floor.

"Reckon you'll have to excuse him—he ain't housebroke," said 'Lias, glowering at the luckless Sonny.

Scarlet with misery, Sonny raised pleading brown eyes to me.

"Doesn't matter a bit," I said consolingly. "Tablecloths are a nuisance anyway. Let's not bother with one."

The men looked relieved, and the dinner was dished up on the bare boards of the kitchen table.

The large serving platters of fried chickens and vegetables were placed on the table, and an invitation to help themselves issued.

In complete silence nine chickens vanished like snow in a blast furnace, and before I had time to start on my own modest helping, the plates were polished clean except for little piles of well-picked bones and one small potato left on Joel's plate.

"Will you have some more vegetables?" I asked, looking at the empty plates in dismay.

Joel pushed back his chair, loosened his belt and picking up his fork spanked the solitary potato with it.

"I've had enough, and that potato's not done," he said.

"Oh!" I murmured apologetically.

"Guess we'll be getting along," said 'Lias, rising reluctantly.

"You haven't had your pudding yet."

The four seated themselves again happily, picked up their spoons and set to. In five minutes all trace of the dessert had vanished from sight.

"That sure tasted good," said Blackie, looking hopefully around.

"I'm sorry we can't offer you any more," said Jerry, looking uncomfortably at me. "I think we ate it all."

"Well, guess we'll be going then," and the four men rose to their feet and filed out as silently as they had come in.

Sonny, the last to leave, turned at the doorway and blushing in confusion said, "I'm sure sorry I messed up your tablecloth."

"Don't think a thing about it, Sonny. It's so easy to upset a glass. Jerry and I are always doing it," I lied politely.

After we had watched them row away up the lagoon, we turned back to the devastated dining table.

138

"For Pete's sake, boil me an egg. I'm starved!" complained Jerry, feverishly buttering a piece of bread. "All I was able to grab was a neck and a piece of liver, and I never got near enough to the peach pudding to even smell it."

"I'll make some tea and I think there's some bacon left," I replied, lifting the stove lid and piling on wood. "The place looks as if a flock of locusts had passed through; but at least we got rid of the roosters."

Chapter 8

To MAKE UP for our failure in animal husbandry, we tried to be as economical as possible in other ways. Guided by Sundi, we had experimented with meals of wild plants and had found most of them to be decidedly unpalatable.

"I really can't see that we save much money by eating this hodge-podge," grumbled Jerry, turning over a watery green mess on her plate. "After all, the only thing we *do* spend money on is food, and surely we can afford to go on doing that until we get properly organized."

Rebellion reached its height when Sundi walked in one day with an armful of what she insisted were edible fungi.

"How do you know they are fit to eat?" I demanded, looking at them with horror. "They are a frightful colour; they could be poisonous."

"You eating them and finding out," explained Sundi with a bland smile. "If they making you sick then they not fit to eating."

"There's going to be no more of this kind of nonsense," declared Jerry when Sundi had gone and the fungi had been thrown out on the garbage heap. "From now on we order our supplies once a month from town and Keijo can go and jump in the lake for all I care."

We gave up scouring the woods for food but there were other economies practised by the islanders which we observed and imitated. Planks and pieces of finished lumber washed up by the tide were carefully dried out and stacked for any future building. Iron dogs, spikes and odd pieces of metal found on old logging sites were straightened out and saved; cardboard cartons and string that came with the groceries were stored away. Empty cans were burned in the kitchen stove and piled on the compost heap along with the ashes and seaweed.

"In time they rotting away and making good soil," said Keijo.

A glass jar or bottle was never thrown away. Sundi showed us how they could be used over and over again.

The prodigal waste of civilization never touched the island. There was a use for everything.

The fishermen had by now returned to the island, full of news and brimming over with tales of their experiences, and once again mail day saw the long, slender fishing boats, rust-streaked and battered from the buffetings of storms, glide out of their dark coves and inlets. The sight of the Dutchman's ash-blond hair and the sound of his hearty laugh as he held out his hands in greeting gave us a warm feeling of belonging to a large and friendly family.

"Ach, but you should haff been wit' me," he cried, "I show you how I catch vun big octopus."

"Did you really? An octopus! How big was it?"

"He muss be eighteen feet across. He tear my nets bigosh. I giff him to Indian, they sure haff goot time eating him."

"*Eating* him?" I exclaimed in disgust. "Do people eat octopus?"

"Sure," said Joel, spitting idly over the side of the boat, "lots of people do. They cut the tentacles into pieces, pound them with rocks and fry them. Taste good too."

"Ugh, how revolting," I said with a shudder.

"What's so bad about it? They eat snails in some places, don't they? What's the difference?"

"I suppose there really isn't any difference," I admitted.

Besides the adventure of the Dutchman's octopus, one of the

fishermen had lost his boat and barely escaped with his life when the engine failed during a storm and the boat drifted up onto the rocks.

"It was two days before they picked me up," he laughed, "and it rained all the time. I was wet and goddam hungry and all I could think about was the pan of good stew that went down with the boat."

"How does it feel to be shipwrecked?" I inquired curiously.

"You don't have time to feel," was the laconic reply, "you're too busy."

Two of the transient fishermen whose names we had never discovered did not return at all. Their boat had been lost in a squall and despite days of searching by the other boats, no trace of them had been found.

I remembered them vaguely—two pale, quiet men who had pooled their savings and gone into partnership. This had been their first trip.

The fact that I had seen and spoken to them so lately brought the manner of their death vividly before my eyes. I had a mental picture of the stormy empty sea, the gale-driven clouds, and the sinking ship.

"It seems such a lonely way to die," I said to Magnus who had listened gravely to an account of the tragedy.

"Death is always lonely however it comes," was his quiet answer.

By this time our social contacts had begun to extend beyond the bounds of the mail-day gatherings. Earlier in the year we had entertained a few of the hardier of our city friends when, their curiosity aroused by the rapturous letters we had sent back home, they had ventured out to inspect our island paradise.

Warned the week before of their impending arrival, we would row gaily out to meet the steamer and be confronted with our guests, garbed in a variety of garments according to their various ideas as to what the well-dressed pioneer should wear.

The costumes ranged all the way from tailored suits, hats, high heels, gloves and cowhide luggage to haversacks, berets and undersized slacks stuffed with oversized posteriors.

The tailored-suiters usually had their fill of pioneering when they looked over the steamer's side and got their first glimpse of the row-boat wallowing about below and saw the grinning faces of the crew who were waiting to lower them into it. They decided on the spot to remain aboard for the round trip and take themselves and their high heels and cowhide luggage back to town.

One or two of the slacked and haversacked visitors made the descent into the row-boat, laughing in a determined fashion and casting scared glances at the waves. The trip through the rapids speedily quenched their mirth and they arrived at our property oblivious to everything but the necessity of getting their feet on dry land again.

Their first remark on arrival was not, as might have been expected, "How beautiful!" but a request in tones of extreme urgency to be shown the quickest way to the john.

"There isn't any!" we would answer brightly.

"There—*what?* . . . What on earth do you do?"

"Oh, just go into the woods and find a tree. There's lots of them."

From then on, the visit was foredoomed to failure. The beauties of the scenery failed to make up for the lack of plumbing, and the thought of the return trip through the rapids hung like a cloud over their disconsolate heads.

By now we were the proud possessors of running water. Keijo had connected our water pipe to the dam on the lake and our domestic water supply came through six hundred feet of rambling galvanized piping that ran through the forest and down the hillside to finish up outside the back door. We had only to walk a few feet and turn a tap to get all the water we needed. After months of bucketing it from the lake, we regarded ourselves as highly civilized when the installation was finished, therefore we were hardly prepared for the disgusted bewilderment of our guests when they were confronted with a bar of soap, a towel and instructions to "wash under the tap."

"Don't you ever have a bath?" they wanted to know.

"Yes. We bathe in the sea. What better bath could a person have?"

The climax usually came at night when we escorted them up the dark mountain trail to the cabin, now converted into a guest-house.

"Aren't there any locks on the doors?" they would ask, appalled.

"Heavens, no! We don't need locks here. Just leave your door open, the air is lovely at night."

As we turned back down the hill, we would hear the sound of a door slam and then numerous articles of furniture being piled up against it.

At breakfast time our guests would appear, pale, heavy-eyed and strangely silent. Careful questioning generally gave us a pretty clear picture of a night spent lying with taut nerves, listening to a silence such as they had never imagined, when a fir cone dropping on the roof was translated into the tread of a bear, and the lonely cry of an owl became the nocturnal howling of a wolf.

Before breakfast was over, we usually found an opportunity to mention in a casual way that the steamer made its return trip to town in two days' time, and the panic-stricken pioneer took the hint gratefully and forthwith departed to the land of flush toilets, electric lights and the familiar and comforting sounds of streetcars and automobile horns.

The friends from the city came no more, but we began to receive calls from residents of other islands and of small communities on the mainland. As we became acquainted with more members of the sparse and migratory population, the news of the two slightly crazy women who were lapping up life the hard way brought us visits from strange specimens of humanity, all anxious to meet with what they fondly hoped would be kindred spirits. We came to realize more and more that the remote portions of the earth attracted a type of humanity that could only be described as misfits—men who harboured a permanent grudge against mankind, recluses, religious fanatics, and cheerful philosophers who believed it was their mission to reform the world.

When we had refused an invitation to join a newly formed religious group which worshipped as its supreme god a Negro of unsavoury reputation and most unpleasant aspect, and had turned down another invitation to become charter members of a proposed small and exclusive colony devoted to nudism and moonlight calisthenics, they left us severely alone.

"A colony!" said Jerry in tones of deep disgust, looking after our latest departing guest, a three-hundred-pound Swede, "—the sight of *that* doing a spring dance in the moonlight would scare the stuffing out of any colony."

By degrees we found ourselves back where we had started and our circle of friends, with two exceptions, was confined once again to the little group which gathered once a week to meet the mail steamer.

The two exceptions were men of widely different type. One was an old Scottish engineer who lived a hermit-like existence on the east coast of the island with no company for miles around other than that of a tame deer.

Hearing him mentioned casually one mail day, Jerry and I pricked up our ears. The remark was to the effect that no-one had seen Angus about lately.

"Who's Angus?" we inquired curiously.

"Oh, he lives over there," with a vague gesture which embraced the whole outdoors.

"What does he do?"

"Fishes—when he is well enough."

"Doesn't anyone ever go to see him?"

Silence and a shrug of massive shoulders greeted this question.

"Supposing he is sick?"

More shrugs and silence.

"Shall we go and see if he is all right?"

The answer to this was that Angus "didn't like folk."

We questioned Sundi on the matter when we arrived back home.

"It's no use going to see him," she said, "he not liking women—especially women who wearing shorts," with a sidelong glance at our abbreviated garments.

"We'll wear slacks then," said Jerry.

"He not liking to see you," persisted Sundi.

145

"I'll bake him a cake," I announced happily. "I bet he never has any."

Sundi made an uncomplimentary grimace.

"He chasing you off place with gun," she said.

"I'm going anyway," I answered.

Next day, we baked the cake, wrapped it up carefully, put on our slacks and prepared to go visiting.

"Shall I take the .22," I asked, mindful of the recent warning, "in case we have to shoot our way out?"

"No," replied Jerry, "we'll take a chance, but we had better leave the dogs at home in case we have to run for it."

We pushed the boat off the beach, climbed in and set out, pursued by a chorus of outraged canine howls.

It was a cool grey day. The sea, looking like a mirror of polished steel, was dotted with clusters of waterfowl. Under the vigorous strokes of the oars the little boat danced over the water and in less than an hour we came to the bay where the Scotsman lived.

We saw his fishing boat tied up to a small wharf, and resting on our oars, we let the skiff drift in while we looked in amusement at the peaked roof of his cabin which showed through the trees.

Leaky roofs were a common complaint on the island, and their owners were prepared to go to any lengths to avoid the bother of a complete reroofing job. Angus had solved his problem by covering the whole of one side with oilcloth patterned in a red and yellow tile effect. The result was startling to say the least.

We drew up to the wharf and I tossed the mooring rope onto the rotting boards.

"You go first," I said valiantly.

Jerry took the rope, tied it to an iron spike and picked her way carefully through the jumble of fisherman's gear which littered the wharf—rusty anchors, empty gasoline drums, paint cans, strings of cork floats, and torn nets. Used as I was to the sight, I stopped to look with fascination at the collection and to peep inside the immaculate boat, before following Jerry up the runway.

Rather timidly we pushed our way through the lilac bushes

which surrounded the cabin and came to the foot of the verandah steps.

Lying on the verandah like a large dog and watching us with soft liquid eyes was a young deer, and behind in the open doorway sat the recluse.

We were prepared to beard the lion in his den, so it came as a complete surprise to find the lion to be nothing more dangerous than a shy, sandy-haired old man who stood in his cabin door blinking his pale eyes at us and smiling wistfully.

"Naebody ever comes tae see me," he said sadly after we had introduced ourselves. "I hae nae-one to talk to—only ma buck," pointing to the deer. "If ye shoot ma buck, I'll kill ye!" he finished in a sudden outburst of ferocity.

"We don't like killing things," I said; and anxious to ingratiate myself, I lost no time in informing him of the Scottish strain in my blood, taking care not to mention the fact that it was considerably diluted by various other strains not so desirable.

"Ah weel—I'm sae pleased tae see you I no can mind my manners. Come in, come in, and I'll mak' ye a dish o' tay."

He ushered us hospitably into his house, which was a picture of disorder. He gave us to understand that when things got too bad, he picked the first windy day, opened all the doors and windows and removed himself to his boat until the wind had blown all the dust and cobwebs out of the house.

The cabin consisted of two rooms and a store shed. The store shed was a regular magpie's nest of assorted articles which he had bought at auction sales at different times. Old clothes, green with age and mildew; sewing-machines, all broken; odd boots, bits of machinery and firearms that had taken his fancy.

In one of the two rooms was a huge old-fashioned kitchen range smothered with grease and rust; a table strewn with the leavings of numerous meals, including a bowl of stewed rhubarb which was beginning to sprout feathers; some broken ship's biscuit, a bottle of sour milk, and a shaving-mug and brush covered with old soapsuds and beard.

147

Pictures of his mother in white mutch and shawl adorned the walls, along with highly and impossibly coloured lithographs of the Scottish highlands.

The bedroom was chiefly filled with bed, covered with a tangle of grey blankets. Underneath the bed could be seen a box of preserved eggs, a case of tinned milk, some ancient and aromatic rubber boots, and that medieval piece of bedroom furniture commonly known as a "thunder mug."

The pride and joy of Angus's heart turned out to be an ancient gramophone which stood by the bedside, together with several boxes of pipe-band recordings. The pleasure he derived from this horror was so great that it apparently never dawned on him that other people might not appreciate it; and in no time at all we found ourselves sitting on the bedroom floor drinking boiled tea out of cracked cups and politely suffering all the agonies produced by a band of bagpipers heard on a thirty-year-old gramophone.

Angus's eyes glistened with emotion as the appalling sounds rang out.

"Aye, and thot's the Sivinty-Second Hielanders leavin' Glasgy," he remarked after a two-minute blast of discord; "and this," he went on proudly, starting another record, "this is the Forty-Second Rigimint enterin' Edinbro."

Jerry and I looked at each other disconcerted. To us, the two records sounded exactly alike.

"Do they all play the same tune?" I asked.

"Na, na—deeferent rigiment, deeferent tune."

"Oh, I see," I murmured politely, not seeing at all and craning my neck to find out how many more records there were in the box.

"Noo I'll gie ye ane o' Harry Lauder's—John, John, John, gang and pit yer troosers on."

"Sounds as if the party is getting rowdy," murmured Jerry in a hurried aside.

I turned to Angus hurriedly. "Haven't you got 'The Flowers of the Forest'? I like that one."

"Och aye," he replied, rummaging among the boxes of records,

148

"I hae that yin too—played by the band of the Cameron Hielanders."

Angus cranked up the machine and let the needle down tenderly on the record, and the room echoed with all the sounds of a gigantic pig-killing.

"Gosh, it sounds awfully like the Seventy-Second Highlanders leaving Glasgow," said Jerry in bewilderment.

"There's naethin' like it," said Angus, looking lovingly at the machine.

"No, there certainly isn't," I answered truthfully, getting up from the floor. "We'll have to go now," I added with well-simulated regret.

"Ye'll no be gangin' awa the noo—there's mair records yet," cried Angus.

"Next time we come, we will hear the whole lot," I said, carefully avoiding Jerry's eye.

"We will do no such thing," said Jerry once we were out of Angus's hearing. "Tinned bagpipes! Ouch!"

Our visit to Angus broke down his crust of reserve; and although he later admitted to us that the excitement caused by our unexpected appearance had kept him awake the whole of the night, he returned our visit one day and ventured into the lagoon, his fishing boat loaded with little gifts. There were pumpkins from his garden, an odd-shaped sea shell which he had picked up on some foreign shore, a load of pine knots for our stove—and of course his cherished gramophone, with which he proposed to delight our ears.

On that occasion we were saved by the timely appearance of Keijo, and Angus, wilting under his wintry gaze, subsided bashfully into a corner, the gramophone forgotten.

Unlike most of the tight-lipped men on the island, Angus made no secret of his past life. He told us that he had been married once, but his wife had died, leaving him with one son.

"What happened to your son?" I inquired.

"Och," replied Angus with a snort of contempt, "he married an English bitch."

"Does he ever come to see you?" I asked.

The old man shook his sandy head and his watery blue eyes

looked sad. The English bitch liked city life and she saw to it that his son stayed away.

During the winter months the friendship between Angus and ourselves grew. We visited his cabin and listened politely to his records. His eager smile when he saw us pushing our way through the lilacs round his home was reward enough for the torture we suffered during these noisy sessions.

He was too shy to come to us and risk a meeting with the dour Keijo or with the Nelsons, who regarded him with good-natured contempt; but we occasionally found little gifts lying on our beach which he had brought in during the night—an oarlock to replace one which had been lost; a few old magazines, hopelessly out of date. Once, after he had heard us complain about the loss of a favourite salmon spoon, we found another exactly like it, complete with line and lead, hanging from the branch of a tree.

The other men on the island listened to our talk of Angus's kindness with wondering looks. The fact that they were all coated with a thick protective armour of reserve themselves had prevented them from discovering the very real loneliness that lay beneath the old Scot's crusty exterior.

"I don't know what you see in him. He's a bad-tempered old coot," said Joel.

"He is not. He is just lonely. You ought to go and see him sometimes," I said angrily.

"I went in there once," said Blackie, "wanted to borrow his bluestone tank. He was going to shoot me because I had a gun—thought I was after his bloody deer."

Besides Angus, we made another friend. This was another hermit but of a very different type.

We had first heard of him from Keijo, who regarded him with complete disapproval. This in itself was a recommendation and we begged immediately for an introduction.

"He talking—talking—talking," said Keijo, spreading out his hands. "Always he is talking—he never stopping."

"That's a change," I said sarcastically. "I'd like to meet him."

"I taking you to see him one day," answered Sundi with a genial smile.

"Is it far? How about tomorrow?" said Jerry, who believed in prompt action.

"If *he* say we can going, we going."

"He" having given a grudging assent to the plan, the next morning saw us packing a picnic lunch and setting off in Keijo's power boat to pay a call on the talkative stranger.

An hour's ride brought us to our destination, which was a small horseshoe-shaped bay on the other side of the island. There were no high canyon walls enclosing a torrent of raging water to block the way to casual intruders and ensure peace and privacy. The entrance to this bay was blocked in a different way, by a huge rock, barely visible below the shallow water, on which the unwary had left noticeable souvenirs in the shape of propeller blades. Sundi showed us the hidden channel, through which we drifted slowly to a white clamshell beach.

"Old Indian reserve, eh?" I asked knowingly, looking at the shells.

Sundi shivered and laughed a little. "It having what you call spooks," she whispered.

"It *does* look a little haunted," I said, looking round uneasily. "Fancy anyone wanting to live alone here!"

We tied the boat to a log on the beach and followed Sundi up a steep path through the woods. A twenty-minute walk through green aisles of fir and hemlock followed. It was a blowy day; the wind rushed through the trees and they swayed and moaned above us. Grouse flew across the trail and hidden animals stirred in the tall ferns.

"What a paradise for hunters!" said Jerry, looking avidly around.

"He not shooting," said Sundi, looking back over her shoulder. "He saying animals should live in peace."

"Quite right," I agreed, plodding along behind. "How much farther do we have to go? I'm tired."

"We there now," said Sundi, and with that, we came to the end of the trail and entered a stand of mighty fir trees that towered above our heads. The straight, unbranching trunks, covered with rugged bark, stretched far up into a spreading canopy of tree-tops. All about us was a dim twilight pierced through here and there with arrows of sunlight. Our footsteps were suddenly deadened in a carpet of thick brown needles and the wind lost itself in the heavy foliage overhead as we stopped, awed by the silence.

"Just look," said Jerry, pointing, "—Hansel and Gretel's gingerbread house!"

I looked and saw, set back among the trees, a squat log building with a weatherbeaten shake roof, tiny odd-shaped windows, and a Dutch door.

As we stood looking at it, a queer gnomelike creature came out of the entrance. He was not much more than five feet in height, and was dwarfed still more by the enormous spread of his shoulders. Horny bare feet protruded from his rolled-up trouser legs, and his sunburnt torso was bare.

My eyes, travelling upward, came to rest on a well-shaped head covered with a mat of shaggy black hair, from under which peered a pair of shrewd grey eyes. A weird assortment of features included thin, rather sensitive lips and a large bulbous nose. I thought he was quite the ugliest man I had ever seen.

He advanced towards us and Sundi greeted him in her own tongue, glancing frequently in our direction.

While she was speaking, the gnome stared at us reflectively and then, extending a welcoming hand, spoke in English in a voice as pleasant as his face was ugly.

"I have heard a lot about you two and the house you have been building. You should have come to see me before; I could have helped you."

"We managed all right," I said awkwardly, "but thanks all the same."

"Come in and see *my* house," said the man, gesturing towards the doorway.

We walked through the open door into a long, low room. The log walls, instead of being chinked with dried moss, had been boarded over and completely pasted with old newspapers. Not an inch but was covered with the news of a decade.

A shallow flight of steps hewn out of split logs ran up the wall at one end and disappeared into a loft. A fireplace like a cave quite filled the wall at the other end.

There was a long refectory table in the room and a variety of settles and chairs with broken springs and ripped upholstery. Small tables littered with books and papers dotted the bare floor. A microscope, field-glasses, a Japanese saki bottle, Indian artifacts, a pair of grinning skulls, dried sea urchins, and the claws of a bear were some of the things that I noticed in my first quick look around.

"How do you like it?' he asked, his thin lips twisting in a smile.

"It's very nice," said Jerry lamely. "What a lovely fireplace!"

Our host grinned wryly.

"I'm disappointed in you," he said. "Why not be honest? You don't like it at all. You like rugs and cushions and curtains and all the rubbish that goes with civilization. You see, I know all about *your* house."

I looked at him warily.

"What's so wrong with our house?"

"Nothing. But I thought you came up here to commune with nature; instead I hear of you polishing cupboards full of silver and brass, and cleaning carpets."

"Whoever told you that told you a lie," I said coldly. "We haven't cleaned a carpet or polished a single thing since we came here. We brought a lot of stuff from the city, I know, but one can be comfortable and still be in harmony with nature."

"A person is never truly in harmony with nature as long as material comforts are a necessity," said the gnome, looking at me with bright intelligent eyes.

"Who said anything about their being a necessity?" I asked irritably. "We just happen to own them, that's all. I've no doubt we could manage to live quite happily if we didn't."

I walked to the open doorway and looked at the shafts of sunlight shining down between the giant trees, and decided to change the subject.

"This is a beautiful spot," I said.

The gnome waved an airy gesture towards the outdoors.

"That is my chapel. That is where I talk to 'Old Whiskers'."

"Old Whiskers?" I repeated, mystified. "Who is he?"

He shrugged his shoulders. "Oh, some people call Him God."

A trifle dazed, I returned to the room, where Sundi was unpacking the lunch basket and laying the contents on the table. She had scorned our offers of tinned-meat sandwiches and heavy cake and had insisted on preparing the lunch herself. It was a triumph of culinary art—fresh sea trout fried in butter, sandwiches of whole-wheat bread and home-made cheese, flaky Danish pastry light as a breeze, and thermos flasks of strong black coffee.

I helped her to clear a space on the table for the food, and glanced at the books as I set them aside. They were written in different languages, but among them were a few that I recognized. Darwin's *Origin of Species* rubbed shoulders with a well-worn English translation of the Koran; Lord Lytton's *The Coming Race* lay on top of the *Meditations* of Marcus Aurelius. With my back turned to the others, I picked up the *Meditations* for a quick glance through the pages. It had obviously been well read and was not there for ornament. I began to feel a profound respect for the strange woodland hermit whom we had come to visit.

While we ate our lunch, our host lived up to his garrulous reputation by keeping up a running stream of conversation. Jerry and I, when we found an opportunity, asked questions, but Sundi, having done her business of introducing us, retired into the background and remained silent.

Among the masses of information which poured out of him, we discovered that his first name was Vaino (his surname we never did succeed in finding out), and his nationality was of such a cosmopolitan nature that he claimed to be a native of eight different countries.

...e can be comfortable and still be in harmony with nature."

'Who's going to milk her?" I asked.
"I am," declared Jerry stoutly.

Three spaniels and a Pekinese.

The two kids, "Horrible" and "Terrible".

"You must have been born somewhere," I said. "Wouldn't the country you were born in be your nationality?"

Vaino told us he had been born in a small village on the Russo-Finnish border, and promptly disclaimed any loyalty to either country. He had lived everywhere and spoke six languages. He had also numbered among his various occupations that of gold miner, farmer, and professor of languages at a famous European university. He had been a sailor also. Besides all this he had been mixed up in several somewhat nefarious enterprises and was acquainted with the inside of more than one jail.

Of his family, if any, he never spoke.

One of his colourful exploits had been a trip round the world in a thirty-foot sloop, about which he had written a book. He showed us a copy of the book, which appeared to be written in extremely flamboyant English and was profusely illustrated with photographs of himself in heroic attitudes.

I listened with awe and admiration. Here at last was one of the picturesque characters about which I had read so often.

Jerry eyed him with a certain amount of dislike and scepticism.

In spite of his arrogance, Vaino had a magnetic personality which drew one in spite of oneself, and some of his philosophy appeared to be sound enough.

"Why wish for money?" he said, when Jerry was bemoaning the fact that the necessity of conserving our financial resources prevented us from buying an engine for our boat. "Set your mind on the thing you want most in life, but never wish for money. That way sorrow lies."

"That's silly," said I, being in an argumentative mood. "There are so many things I want. If I wished for them all separately, life would be over before I got half of them. Now if I wish for a million dollars, one wish will do for the whole lot."

Vaino smiled at me in an indulgent way.

"You'll never get your wishes that way. If you get one thing it is always at the expense of something else. You can't have everything, so *know* what it is you want most from life and then be willing to

155

sacrifice everything else for it; but be very careful that you are quite sure that when you have got your wish, you won't regret it."

He paused and then added in sombre tones:

"Things wished for long enough and hard enough have a disagreeable way of coming true."

"They don't for me," I laughed.

"That is because you don't really know what you want. You waste your energy running from one thing to another."

"Do you know what *you* want?" I asked impudently.

Vaino's face stiffened as he stared into the empty fireplace.

"I thought I did once," he said slowly. He hesitated.

"Did you ever hear the story of the man who was granted three wishes and after he got the first two, his third wish was for death?"

He stood up and his eyes were tormented.

"I was unlucky. I didn't get a third wish."

"It seems to me," I ruminated, "that the catch in all this is that by the time you get what you want, you no longer want it, which all adds up to the fact that if you want to be happy you shouldn't wish for anything."

Vaino's steely grey eyes bored into me.

"You really are learning fast," he said.

He turned away from us and walked to Sundi who was gazing at us with uncomprehending eyes from her corner.

"I am afraid we are neglecting you," he said. "Come along and I'll show you my new storehouse."

For the remainder of the visit, he devoted himself exclusively to the entertaining of Sundi. Chattering amiably in her own tongue, they inspected the storehouse shelves, the winter squash and root vegetables in their sawdust bins, and the well-stocked smoke-house.

Jerry and I wandered through the dark aisles of the forest out to where a large tract of land had been cleared and laid out in pasture for a couple of fine Jersey cows.

The golden haze of Indian summer lay over the land and a faint whiff of scent rose from the pine needles under our feet. In the distance we could hear the faint murmur of the sea. We leaned against the tree trunks and discussed our strange new acquaintance.

"Do you like him?" I asked.

"I don't know," replied Jerry slowly. "I think he could charm the heart out of a rattlesnake, but there is something there I don't quite understand."

We looked at the misty mountains where among dark bands of evergreens the golden maples shot up like tongues of flame.

"Let's go back to the house," said Jerry suddenly.

We found Vaino and Sundi still inspecting storehouse supplies and talking about poultry and cattle. They took no notice of us and we went inside the house, where we roamed aimlessly about looking at the dusty books and the odd miscellany of articles which Vaino had collected in his travels.

"These newspapers on the walls have all been pasted right way up in some sort of order," I said over my shoulder. "There are a lot of pages from books and magazines among them, and editorials and speeches and articles and goodness knows what. I wonder what the idea is?"

Jerry took a look at the print-covered walls and grinned.

"I knew I had heard that yarn about the three wishes somewhere," she said. "You remember that story of Jacob's called 'The Monkey's Paw'? Well, here it is, the whole thing. That must be where he got the idea—though he seems to be a bit mixed up as to who died when the last wish was granted. I bet he sits here and reads this stuff till he believes it has happened to him."

"Here are some more of his ideas," I said, moving to another spot. "Just look at this, word for word."

We walked slowly about the room, looking at the gems of wisdom culled from various sources; and in them we recognized some of Vaino's profound quotations, which he had lifted bodily from their context and apparently delivered as products of his own mind.

We were so busy reading and laughing that we did not hear Vaino enter the room until he spoke.

"I see you are looking at my library," he said.

Jerry and I exchanged a guilty look.

"I don't quite understand," I said.

"It's simple," replied Vaino, quite unabashed. "Whenever I come across an article or theory which I think is worth while, I just paste it on the wall. It is always there for me to refer to and it helps to keep out the draft."

"So your philosophy is all second hand?" Jerry said with a pleased smile.

"All philosophies are second hand," said Vaino calmly. "There are very few original thoughts in the world."

"They must have been original once," I objected.

"Not necessarily," answered Vaino. "Knowledge is handed down from one different incarnation to another and most of us live and die without ever discovering it. Now and then some man rediscovers a great truth and is hailed by the masses as a profound thinker. Actually he is only remembering something that was common knowledge eons ago."

I took a hasty look over my shoulder at the wall behind me.

"Yes," said Vaino, watching me, "try the wall by the fireplace, you will find the source of that remark there."

"Somehow it seems like cheating," I said.

"Why should it?" asked Vaino. "Great teachers base their philosophies on the sayings of some earlier teacher. Why should I pretend to be cleverer than they?"

"There have been people with original theories," I persisted.

"Many people," said Vaino, picking up a book from the table, "but they generally find out they are wrong before they die—that is, if they have the intelligence to realize it and the humility to admit it. That's why half the people in the world are running round in circles. They won't look for the fundamentals. They prefer the trimmings."

We looked at him in silence. We had come prepared for almost anything. A discussion on philosophy by a half-naked dwarf was certainly not among them.

Sundi came in and looked at us with her round blue eyes.

"It time we leaving," she said, "tide turning."

I started to pick up the picnic basket.

"Now that we have met," said Vaino, "I hope that you will come often."

We made non-committal remarks about our being busy and it being a long way to row.

"In that case," said Vaino decisively, "I shall come myself and fetch you."

We left him standing beneath the giant trees in his chapel, the sunlight striking down on his bare shoulders and untidy black hair.

On the way home we plied Sundi with questions about him. Had he any family? Why did he never come out on mail day? Her answers were brief.

"He having no family. He getting no mail."

"Well, he's probably hiding out from the police. You never know in places like this, you seem to run into the queerest people."

We spent the next few days feeling vaguely dissatisfied with our life in the lagoon.

"The boys are awfully kind," I said in discontented tones one day, "but I wish we could talk about something else but fish and turnips once in a while."

"You can always talk about cows with Sundi, or else discuss life 'the hard way' with Keijo," replied Jerry. "You're not hankering for that black-haired ape we met last week, are you?"

Of course not," I said indignantly, but secretly I was not so sure. The brief taste of more intellectual conversation had whetted my appetite for more.

Chapter 9

WE SOON found out that Vaino, having made up his mind to be friendly, was to become a persistent visitor.

Restless and out of his element in the lagoon, where he was regarded with suspicion by the four brothers and with undisguised hatred by Keijo, he used to sweep aside all our objections and insist on our accompanying him back to his ghost-haunted bay, where over cups of muddy cocoa, a drink for which he seemed to have a mysterious partiality, we would hold long discussions. The print on the walls of his house provided the basis for most of our arguments, and the walls being extensive, we never ran short of material for our talks.

The main trouble was that Vaino, with his large assortment of information, could quite easily argue either side of a question according to his mood of the moment, and we frequently came away from his house utterly confused.

It was not only mental stimulus that we gained from our friendship with Vaino. We benefited in other ways too. It was he who knew where the cod banks were, and who showed us where to fish for the tasty red snapper which lurked in the deep holes. He knew also how to concoct a medicinal brew out of wild herbs; he showed us the blisters on the trunk of a balsam tree, and pricking them collected the golden resin which oozed out, telling us that there was no finer medicine for chest colds. He gathered goose grass on the beach and showed us how to cook it in a most palatable way. He showed us wild onions growing on the cliff tops, and a shrub which he called "squaw tea" which he claimed could be brewed into a healthful drink.

In addition to all this, his knowledge of wildlife was immense. We were fascinated by his stories of the habits of wild animals, none of which seemed to have any fear of him. The birds walked into his house, sat on the back of his chair and fed on the crumbs he scattered for them, with no appearance of fright if he moved suddenly.

A family of raccoons came regularly each evening to feed out of his hand, and the squirrels sat on the window-sill peering through the glass for the bits of bread with which he used to feed them.

"If you treat an animal like a human being, it will become almost like one," he used to say; "and don't forget, they can teach us far more than we can teach them." He pointed out to sea where three seagulls were riding on a log, each with one wing spread out.

"Those birds know all about navigation without having to go to school to learn it. They use their wings to steer with. Watch now, when they get round that rock they will change direction."

Watching, we saw all three birds suddenly spread both wings simultaneously, and the log on which they were riding gradually changed course.

"I've often seen them do that, but I never knew why," I said; "in fact, I don't believe I ever thought about it."

"That's what civilization does for you," said Vaino. "It blinds a person to everything but pure materialism."

As our education progressed and Vaino monopolized more and more of our time, our visits to Angus became less frequent.

"I miss ye," he said unhappily on one rare occasion when we had rowed round to his bay. "Why do ye no come tae see me?"

"We have been busy," I answered, turning from the reproach in the old man's eyes, "and the sea has been so rough lately." Then, with a twinge of conscience at our neglect of him, I touched him on the shoulder and added: "When Christmas comes, we will have a real bang-up party, and we will bring you a present."

Angus shook his head wearily.

"I dinna want a present—I juist want ye tae come and talk tae me."

We left him standing in the doorway looking after us with unhappy eyes.

As the autumn gales set in, we found our visiting considerably curtailed. It became an impossibility for us to round the tip of the island and face the full force of the pounding seas in our small boat. Even Vaino, who was an excellent seaman and cared nothing for rough weather, came less often and we found ourselves confined to the lagoon.

We watched the rain driving across the water and the trees clashing together as the wind tore through their branches. The iron stovepipes shook and rattled and showers of pine needles fell on the roof and seeped through the cracks in the shakes and lay over everything.

Sometimes at night we would be roused from sleep by the shrieking winds, and sitting up in our cots would cover our ears with our hands, trembling with fright as the solid log house creaked in the gale. Between the gusts would come a lull which always seemed more frightening than the roar of the storm.

"Will it be like this all winter?" we asked the Nelsons.

"This is only the beginning," they answered, "but when the storm season is over, we will have a calm spell before winter really sets in."

"You mean it will be worse than this?" I asked in trepidation.

"The snow and ice have to come yet," answered Joel easily. "We may be frozen in."

With November, the storms increased in violence, and we saw our blue smiling sea turn into a ravening monster. Gale-force winds swept across the island in screaming fury, blowing the long strands of rain before them. The surface of the lagoon was dark and troubled and flecked with foam, while out beyond the entrance was a grey hell of storm-driven cloud and spray, where waves like great beasts flung themselves at the stolid cliffs and fell back shattered and hissing.

Under these conditions there was no comfort for any of us. The constant roar of the elements coupled with the loud rattling of windows and stove-pipes frayed our nerves. The smoke from the fires puffed out into the room until our eyes were red and smarting.

The dogs, uneasy and whimpering, shrank from the gusts which buffetted the house, and outside on the porch the goats, with rank, dripping fur, huddled together in terror.

"I think it's the noise that is the worst part of it," complained Jerry one day. "You know, I have an idea that hell would be a place where there was a constant gigantic noise. What do you think, Joel?"

Joel looked blank.

"I dunno," he said indifferently. "Don't know as I've ever thought about it."

One storm followed on the heels of another, and the roaring and rattling continued. Giant trees crashed in the forest behind us and loose branches whirled over the house-top.

"Now's the time to look out for widow-makers," said Joel. "Don't you go walking about in the woods when she's blowing like this."

At intervals during the clearing periods, we saw the mountain tops emerge briefly from the clouds, only to be hidden again in a short time by grey, shifting masses of vapour. Each time we saw them, we noticed that the snow had crept a little further down their sides, and we shivered before the relentless march of winter.

Occasionally there would be a complete cessation of the hideous roaring, when the elements seemed to pause before gathering all their resources together for another outburst. When this happened, we seized the opportunity of rowing out into the lagoon and visiting our neighbours.

Wrapped in oilskin slickers, with knee-high rubber boots and sou'westers, we sat in the wet boats, rowing and baling while the cold rain poured down our backs.

163

The islanders took the weather as they took everything else, in their stride, and the storms which worried us caused them little or no concern.

"Shucks, this is nothing," said 'Lias; "a sixty-mile-an-hour wind is only a breeze compared to what it can do when it likes."

With the first coming of the winter gales, we had worried about the mail and supplies.

"What shall we do?" asked Jerry anxiously. "We can't possibly go out in this."

"*You* can't, but don't let that fret you," said 'Lias calmly. "We'll bring in the mail while we can. Later on there'll be times when no-one can get out. Better you should stock up on supplies against those times."

Heeding their advice, we stocked up on flour, sugar and canned goods, and while the winter storms raged outside, we stayed snug and safe inside the lagoon while the four brothers braved the raging seas and brought in our mail whenever it was possible, and shrugged off our grateful thanks.

"Shucks," they said, blushing and embarrassed, "it's nothing. We're glad to do it. Reckon you'd do the same for us."

Sundi, storm-bound like ourselves and hungering for companionship, would sometimes drop in carrying a jug of fresh cream, and over our coffee cups tell us stories of life in Finland—stories of long, cold winter nights in a strange frozen world of stars and flashing northern lights; stories of Laplanders driving their reindeer sleighs to market at breakneck speed over the snow. She described how the sleighs in the mad racing frequently rolled completely over and righted themselves again with their drivers still in them, the reindeer never pausing in their galloping stride.

We listened, fascinated.

On our return visits, we were invited to partake of a sauna or steam bath. All Finlanders have a steam bath on the premises, and use it regularly. We discovered that it was regarded as a social error not to invite one's friends in for a bathing party.

"Just like afternoon tea in England," said Jerry to me.

164

On our first visit to the bath-house we found that it was not at all like afternoon tea in England. A Finnish bath party consisted of a number of large, naked Scandinavians sitting in a row round the walls of a tiny overheated wooden cell, beaming with happiness and dripping with sweat.

Keijo's bath-house was built on the rocks above the sea and consisted of two rooms, the steam-room and a dressing-room. The steam-room was small and hot. The dressing-room was small and cold.

In the first stood a fire-box of brick and on it stood a forty-gallon oil drum filled with scrap iron. When the fire underneath was lit, the whole drum and its metal contents glowed white-hot.

In the wall was a tap with a piece of rubber hose attached to it. That was the shower. For the rest, there was a row of wooden benches rising in tiers from floor to roof.

In a community where the female of the species was regarded as being of considerably less importance than the male, the men took their steaming first, and the women patiently waited for the leavings.

Jerry and I, summoned to the party, used to sit by the window in Keijo's sun-porch and watch the lords of creation, boiled to a lobster red, erupt out of the bath-house in their shorts and totter off in a collapsed condition to cool themselves by rolling about in the icy sea water. Then, shepherded by Sundi, we took our turn.

The process of steam-bathing commenced in the dressing-room, where we took off all our clothes and marched stark naked into the steam-room. Here, in company with any other visiting females, we sat in a solemn row on the lowest of the wooden benches that lined the walls.

The heat from the fire-box in that confined space was suffocating and our discomfort increased when Sundi threw buckets of water over the red-hot boiler, sending stinging rushes of steam to the roof and enveloping the guests.

When the party began to gasp for air, a wet cloth was placed over the mouth and nose to facilitate breathing, and the whole group moved up one bench higher.

Bunches of twigs were provided at this point with which the bathers belaboured each other heartily in order to bring the blood to the surface; and soon a river of sweat was flowing down each beaten and scalded body. That was the signal for a general move up to a still higher bench, the rules of the game being to see who could reach the top bench first and stay there the longest.

The top bench, hidden in the clouds of floating steam, was the supreme test of endurance and only the hardiest bather could aspire to those heights. Jerry and I, suffering acutely, actually never rose beyond ground level and were regarded with good-natured contempt by Sundi, who seemed to have the constitution of a salamander.

After the decree had passed that we had been sufficiently boiled, a further form of torture awaited us in the shape of a stream of ice-water pouring out of the hose. This, driving down on our steam-scalded skin, never failed to evoke squeals of anguish and was an ordeal which we always tried to escape; but there was no escaping Sundi, standing in a cloud of steam like a giant Brunnhilde and swinging the hose. The spray of icy water found us in whatever corner we tried to hide.

"You cannot going out without shower," said she, "you catching cold."

Catching cold was an unheard-of thing in our locality, and was something that happened to the islanders only when they had a rare visitor from the outside world. On those occasions, although the visitor might himself be free of a cold, all the islanders immediately caught one, the germs seeming to spread like magic among the residents.

On these occasions, Keijo retired with suppressed wrath and a bottle of rum to his bath-house and boiled himself back to health, and the rest of the inhabitants sniffled, with their usual patience, until the cold had run its course.

While the storm season continued, we thought frequently of Angus and Vaino. Inquiries made to Joel and his brothers brought only a shake of the head; hardly anyone ventured out in this weather and the mail-day gathering had virtually ceased to exist.

166

"What do they do about their mail?" I asked one day.

"It goes back to town till the weather calms down; there's nothing so important that it won't keep."

"I wouldn't have thought so once," I mused, "but somehow since I came to live here I am finding out that nothing *is* really important any more."

In a few weeks the storms blew themselves out and calm once again settled over our little world. The sea flattened out and the sun shone once again, paler than before but with sufficient warmth to make our outdoor tasks a pleasure.

The weekly trips out to meet the mail steamer were resumed and we found the group of boats and their colourful occupants once again gathered behind the rocky islands off the coast; and, to the accompaniment of straining anchor cables and creaking timbers, we heard the different fishermen relate their experiences during the storm season.

According to them, the weather had been unusually severe and the floats had been badly damaged. Dinghies had been washed away and fishing boats pounded by floating logs. The men living on the outside had spent night after night sitting up to guard their boats and watching to see that the mooring ropes and cables held during the storm. The Dutchman had broken two ribs when he slipped on the wet planks of his float. His woman had bound him up with strips made from old sugar sacks and next day he had gone out and split half a cord of wood.

The accident had done nothing to quench his high good humour, although his hearty laugh was a little less frequent.

"You no tell me foony stories no more," he warned, shaking a thick finger at me. "Bigosh, it hurt too damn mooch to laugh."

Pat, the postmaster, had spent a few days in the city and was full of his adventures. Most of his time had been spent in different east-end beer parlours, where his unusual headgear had excited some unflattering comments. A missing front tooth and a suspicious discolouration around one eye testified to the lengths to which Pat had allowed his resentment to carry him.

More important than the fighting over his hat was the fact that he had managed to pick up a "lady" on his trip down on the steamer. The obvious difficulty of trying to tell all the details of his amorous adventure to the other men when Jerry and I were present, led him to bring his story to a most fantastic climax.

The "lady," he insisted, had been a "real lady," as shown by the feathers in her hat, the fact that she wore gloves, and "some kind of smelly stuff on her." They had dined at the same table and walked the deck together, and at night he had gallantly escorted her to her cabin, which happened to be next to his own.

At this point, Pat paused uneasily. No comments were forthcoming from any of us. The other men gazed innocently out to sea, and apart from one or two faint smirks, their expressions remained unchanged. Pat glanced sideways at us, took a thoughtful pull at his pipe and went on with his yarn.

After he had gone to bed, he had heard a tapping on the wall that divided the two cabins, and when he went to inquire what the trouble was, the "lady" had informed him that she was nervous and unable to sleep.

Another uneasy pause.

"Well?" I said impatiently, thinking that the tale was being dragged out unnecessarily.

"Faith, an' I couldn't leave her alone in that state, could I now?"

"Of course not. What did you do?"

Pat glanced out of the corner of his eye at the bland faces of the fishermen; then, looking back at us with a defiantly virtuous expression, he made the epic statement:

"Sure an' I read to her till dawn."

It says much for the rigid control of the islanders that not one of them even smiled.

Occasionally now, Vaino came out of his lonely cove to join the group. We never saw him receive any mail other than newspapers, but his presence added a sprightliness to the conversation that had been lacking before. With the fishermen he seemed to be popular and only Joel and his brothers and Keijo kept aloof and looked at him with cold suspicion. With Keijo, this was understandable—he disliked everybody and was in turn equally disliked; but Joel was tolerant and we could not understand his attitude.

"Why don't you like him, Joel?" I asked one day.

"He talks too damn much," answered Joel shortly.

To me, this seemed no reason at all, and cautiously I sounded out Vaino as to his feelings towards our neighbours.

"The boys have been so kind to us since we came here," I said, feeling my way. "They are very nice."

"Very nice," agreed Vaino with a faintly ironic smile; "an apt description. A little colourless perhaps, but very nice."

"Don't you like nice people?" I asked, bristling a little.

"Not particularly. I find them usually very stupid."

He walked away, leaving me puzzled and angry, because as always there was a germ of truth in his remark.

Taking advantage of the calm weather, we rowed up the coast to see Angus. Pushing our way through the leafless lilacs, we found him sitting quietly in the open doorway of his cabin. His hands were folded on his lap and his eyes rested fondly on the deer, which lay on the grass in front of the verandah steps. His face lighted up at the sight of us.

"So ye came at last. I thocht ye had forgotten me."

"We brought you some home-made bread," said Jerry. "It turned out good this time."

"Ye are always bringin' me things and I canna do onything in return," cried Angus, overwhelmed with gratitude. "Sit ye doon, sit ye doon."

Our arrival, as usual, gave Angus an excuse to set the gramophone playing and to pour more water from the smoke-blackened kettle into the teapot that stood eternally on the stove.

As we drank our bitter tea and listened to the squeals of the gramophone I noticed how pale and worn the old man looked.

"Och, it's juist a bit of a cough," he said when questioned.

"You should go and live with your son, Angus," we told him. "You shouldn't be living up here by yourself."

Angus looked aghast.

"What? Live wi' yon English bitch?" he said. "Na, na, I've allus kept mysel' to mysel' and I wunna be beholden to onyone."

He looked at us wistfully as we were leaving.

"Ye wunna be lang afore ye come again?"

We promised to come whenever the weather was fine, and he followed us down to the boat coughing painfully. We headed into the waves outside Angus's little bay filled with vague worryings about him.

The next day was mail day, and was recorded in the unwritten annals of the island as the day on which Magnus lost his boat.

It was a sullen wet day, and the boats congregated out at sea huddled together in the lee of the rocks, their little stove-pipes smoking cheerfully. Jerry and I, our skiff tied up to the Dutchman's boat, were sitting in his cabin watching him shave a piece of cedar into fine fragments for kindling.

One end of the stick was sliced with his pocket knife until it branched out in all directions like the petals of a flower.

"Now I shoost hold de odder end in my handt. Zo! Poosh heem in de stove. Zo! Now I light de match."

At that precise moment a terrific explosion occurred outside.

"Mein Gott!" exclaimed the startled Dutchman. "Vot vos dat?"

Jerry and I leapt up the cabin steps and out on the deck, and saw flames shooting up into the air from Magnus's boat. Through the smoke we dimly saw him beating vainly at them with sacks. As we watched, another explosion shook the boat and Magnus was blown over the rail into the sea. The whole interior of the boat became a raging inferno and a great panic seized the occupants of the other boats as they hastened to pull up their anchors and move to a safe distance.

"Get back—get back before the other tank goes up!" shouted Joel as his boat with reversed engines roared noisily past us.

The deck on which we stood was already vibrating with the throb of the engine, and even as Joel spoke, the Dutchman bounded past us, hauled up the anchor and dived back into the wheel-house.

In a daze as we backed away we saw Vaino's powerful speed-boat dash up to the burning vessel, under a shower of sparks and flaming fragments pick up the swimming Norwegian, and dash back to safety.

"How awful! Look how it burns!" I said. "What do you suppose could have happened?"

"Fumes from the gas tanks and an open stove, likely," said 'Lias, who had stepped across the rail of his own boat onto ours.

A third and smaller explosion came, sending a shower of debris high into the air. The flames, crackling and hissing, shot up higher than before and then dropped down to a steady burning.

"That's the spare tank," said 'Lias. "I knew he had another one aboard. I guess it's all over now."

In a little while the flames began to die down and the boat, listing a little, started to settle in the water. Slowly the other boats began to close in and form a circle round the drowning ship, and in silence we stood and watched her slowly sink.

"She doesn't seem to want to go," said Joel as the boat struggled a little in the water.

Looking at the sinking little ship and the ring of boats with their silent occupants, I felt my eyes smart with tears.

"It's like watching a person die," I said.

The water rushing in put out the flames, and with a great hissing and steaming the boat gradually disappeared. One end of a loose plank shot up in the air like a waving hand, hung poised for a moment and then vanished. A life-belt floated to the surface, and then there was nothing but an area of bubbles and charred ash left to mark the grave.

The Dutchman, his eyes fixed on the spot, shook his blond head, his round face serious.

"She vos a goot boat too. I vunder vos she insured?"

The attention of the fishermen had now turned from the sunken boat to its owner, and the dinghies were crowding round Vaino's speed-boat to inquire after Magnus. Speculation was rife as to the value of the boat, the amount of insurance, if any, and the fate of the owner's belongings.

"I know he had five hundred dollars aboard," said Blackie. "It was all the money he had and he kept it with him always. Said it was for his funeral expenses."

Joel rowed out of the cluster of small boats surrounding the speed-boat and came up beside us.

"Is he badly hurt?" asked Blackie.

Joel shook his head; the burns had been superficial and Vaino was attending to them.

"How about the money?"

Joel shook his head again.

"Reckon he didn't have time to save anything, it all happened so fast. Lucky he had that wooden leg; it sort of kept him afloat till Vaino got to him."

"Did he carry insurance?" I asked.

Joel did not think so, and went on to explain that the insurance rates on boats were so high that many fishermen preferred taking a chance to paying out the premiums.

"He still has his mink ranch," said Blackie, "but he had bad luck with the critters last year. He was figuring to make up his losses by going with the fishing fleet next season."

"I am beginning to see what life the hard way means," said Jerry thoughtfully. "What will he do now?"

Blackie shrugged his shoulders.

"He might get a job as whistle punk in a logging camp; he's worked in the camps before, used to be donkeyman. That's how he lost his leg."

"Oh?" I looked up at him. "What happened?"

Blackie's bald statement of the facts was vivid in its simplicity.

Magnus and two other men had been working on the donkey engine when the cable broke and the machine on its heavy sled shot downhill. One man jumped clear; Magnus had his leg crushed so badly that it had to be amputated; and the third man, caught directly in front of the heavy machinery, was left a bloody smear on the ground.

"I was working there at the time," added Blackie. "We found one arm in a bush and the rest of him we just scraped up and put in a sack."

I shuddered. "And you still work in the woods after that?" I asked in horror.

"Buggerall! A feller has to eat," was the laconic reply.

I turned horrified eyes towards the group gathered round Vaino's boat. They were transferring the injured man to one of the larger boats. A burst of laughter came from the cabin where Magnus had been carried, and we saw Vaino step out on deck, his broad shoulders shaking.

Filled with curiosity, Blackie edged his own vessel up beside the others and leaning over the side, loudly demanded to be included in the joke.

"We found the five hundred dollars," said 'Lias with his serious smile.

"Where?"

"In Magnus's wooden leg."

We stared uncomprehendingly, but we found that 'Lias had spoken the truth. Magnus's artificial stump had served a dual purpose as leg and safety-deposit box. Not only the five hundred dollars but the insurance policy for the boat and his naturalization papers were folded in a neat packet in the top of it, forming a cushion for his amputated leg.

Magnus was in high good humour. "It was a lucky day for me when I lost that leg!" he shouted from the bunk where he was lying.

Discussing the event some days later with Vaino, I remarked on the accident that had cost Magnus his leg.

"I should think he's glad that he doesn't ever have to go back to the woods," I said fervently. "If it was me I would be scared to death every minute I was there."

Vaino looked at me thoughtfully.

"Why?"

"*Why?* Because you never know the minute you are going to be killed," I replied.

Vaino grinned wickedly and I immediately regretted the opportunity I had given him to hold forth on one of his favourite topics, namely the tenacity with which he claimed a Christian clings to life.

"Christians!" he said with a derisive laugh. "You build up a wonderful theory of an after-life spent in an eternity of bliss, and you are all scared as hell of going to it."

"Nobody likes the idea of dying," I said impatiently.

"No, and the more civilized a person is, the less he likes it. Just take any heathens—they take death in their stride and don't worry about it; but of course they have nothing much to lose in this life, and that makes a difference."

"Whereabouts on your walls do you keep that idea pasted up?" I asked in a voice dripping with sarcasm.

"Nowhere," laughed Vaino, "that is the result of my own observations. Look around you at the people living here. Heaven is just a fairy-tale to most of them but they aren't afraid of dying. Death loses its terror when people live hand in hand with it. Just think about it some time."

I had occasion to think about it later in the week when one of the fishermen who was doing some part-time work in a camp on the mainland was killed. This time again it was a cable that had broken. Flying back, it had whipped round the man's body, burying itself in the flesh from chest to knee.

"He looked like a boned ham," said Blackie indifferently. "The meat was bulging out between the coils like raw hamburger."

This time the victim had remained conscious long enough to make a few simple requests about the disposition of his belongings and then had died before he could be moved to the first-aid hut.

"I wonder if he was afraid to die?" I said, my mind running on Vaino and his theories.

Blackie looked at me blankly and calmly lit a cigarette.

"Reckon he was hurting so bad, dying must have been a real pleasure."

I looked at Jerry. "You know, pioneering isn't nearly as romantic as I imagined. You need to be a philosopher like Vaino or a hard-bitten hunk of toil like Blackie to be able to face the grimmer aspects of it."

Jerry clasped her hands round her knees and rocked thoughtfully back and forth. I looked out of the window and thought about the man who had looked like a "boned ham." Blackie puffed at his cigarette with unconcern and obviously did not think at all.

In an endeavour to turn my thoughts into pleasanter channels, I jumped up and picked up the kettle.

"How about a cup of coffee, Blackie?"

"Sounds like a right smart idea," said Blackie gratefully. "Talkin's worn blisters on my tongue."

During the next hour Blackie drank seven cups of coffee, ate twenty-one hot cakes with full accompaniment of maple syrup and butter, and said never a word during the process. When the coffee-pot was empty, he wiped his mouth with his sleeve, pushed his chair back and lumbered towards the door.

"Thanks for dropping in, Blackie," I said as he was leaving.

"Yeah," responded Blackie in his dry tones, "reckon we had a real interestin' discussion."

Chapter 10

WHEN THE fall days drew to a close we found ourselves, together with our neighbours, caught up in a fever of winter preparations.

"Get in plenty of wood, and be sure it's dry," said Joel one day. "Nothing worse than trying to start a fire on a cold morning with wet wood."

Taking his advice, we spent a couple of hours every morning on the woodpile, sawing up logs into stove lengths with our rusty cross-cut. Our progress was slow, and we found pleasanter ways of augmenting our fuel supply by picking up dead branches and odd pieces of driftwood on the beach.

Frequently our wood gathering took the form of an occupation known to us as "barking." It commenced with a long row across the lagoon to a spot where loggers at some long-past time had left a bleak, ruined valley. Here, where once giant conifers had spread sheltering arms over a carpet of huckleberry and fern, was now a tangled mass of branches and rotting tree trunks criss-crossed over each other in a riot of confusion. The ferns and berries were crushed and dead, and the little stream which had once run happily through the valley was choked with debris, its normal course diverted into a dozen feeble rills which spilled over into dank pools and bogs.

Among this desolation lay piles of thick, dry bark, bleached almost white with the sun and as hard as flint. We loaded our boats down with sacks of it and stacked it in piles outside the kitchen door. In the stove it burnt like anthracite coal, made a hot glowing fire and left very little ash.

The fact that each expedition was accompanied by a picnic basket and took up most of the day, ending with our rowing home in the stormy sunset singing at the tops of our voices, brought down Keijo's wrath on our heads.

"Winter coming and you wasting time," he said sternly. "All summer you should have salting down fish—you should have canning vegetables."

"What vegetables?" asked Jerry lazily, tilting her yachting cap to the back of her head. "We ate everything that came up, long ago."

"Besides I hate canned vegetables," I added. "We've got lots of potatoes; we'll be all right."

Disregarding the warnings of our neighbours, we continued with our carefree existence, making a game of every necessary household task.

Once a week, bread had to be made. This was always an exciting event because we never could be entirely sure what the results of our efforts would be. Our healthy bodies managed to digest all but the most revolting specimens; and in the few instances where the bread turned out to be of such a consistency as to defy all onslaughts of teeth and knives, it was thrown out to the dogs, who swallowed it unchewed and swelled out proportionately.

Failure in the culinary department bothered us not at all. We ate everything with relish and very often night would find us sitting up in bed with the glow from the fire shining on us while we took bites out of a large chunk of soggy brown bread well soaked with butter, and drank strong cups of coffee. Sometimes a notable addition to this midnight repast would be a piece of cheese as thick as a doorstep, and a large slice of heavy pastry stuffed with dates and brown sugar, hot out of the oven. After this, we would fall back on our pillows and sleep dreamlessly.

One day a week was devoted to washing clothes. No electric washing-machines and dryers here. We carried our laundry up to the lake, built a fire in the open, placed the large square galvanized washtub firmly on it and filled it with water. Dirty overalls and wool socks all went in together, along with sheets, towels and tablecloths, and the lot was boiled furiously until the water was the consistency of pea soup and everything in it reduced to a uniform grey. After this we rinsed the mournful-looking results out in the icy waters of the lake and hung them over the branches of trees to dry.

"They may not look so good, but at least they have been freshened up," said Jerry, undaunted by the spectacle.

Ironing was something we never bothered about except on rare occasions, when we used a flat stone heated in the oven and wrapped in paper.

We rarely did any mending either, so in the course of time we came to resemble a couple of scarecrows more than anything else. Overalls with the legs in shreds, shirts with the sleeves torn out and rips down the backs, holes in the heels of socks and running-shoes with burst toes—all of this, combined with copper-tanned faces and wind-roughened hair, gave us the appearance of two female Huckleberry Finns.

The transition was so gradual, though, that we barely noticed the deterioration of our garments until one mail day, when it was brought sharply to my attention by my noticing a row of grinning passengers who were leaning over the steamer's rail delightedly taking in all the details of Jerry's attire.

On this occasion she was wearing a pair of what had originally been grey flannel slacks. Time and rough usage had left their marks and by now they had been hacked off above the knee and adorned with two large patches of different colours. Her shirt, once white, was ripped from shoulder to waist and had only one sleeve; her running-shoes were split at the toes and laced up with string; a dirty white yachting cap was pulled jauntily over one eye. In this garb she was standing up in the row-boat, hands on hips, and forcefully haranguing the captain of the steamer on the subject of missing freight. The interchange of compliments between Jerry in her rocking skiff and the captain on the bridge added considerable colour to the picture.

"We ought to tidy up a little before going out to meet the mail boat," I said when we were on our way home. "You really look an awful sight."

"You don't look so hot yourself," retorted Jerry, bristling.

"I know," I agreed soberly, "but there is no need for us to go to seed completely just because we live on an island, and that is what will happen if we are not careful."

Our domestic activities were incidental, however, and under Keijo's constant prodding we made determined efforts to live life "the hard way" by frequent fishing and hunting expeditions.

After careful experimenting we had discovered that it was possible for us to negotiate the rapids and avoid the rocks and whirlpools by easing our small boat close to the walls of the canyon where the water ran deep and swift. Sometimes we snagged a rock in passing, and our boats became more and more battered as time went on.

The feeling of fear which we could never quite overcome used to communicate itself to the dogs crouching in the stern. Suey was extremely vocal in expressing his dislike of rapids-shooting. He whimpered and whined, peered over the side of the boat at the tumbling water, and gradually worked himself up into a fit of hysteria which ended in his tumbling under the seat in a screaming, twitching heap.

"Why don't you leave him at home?" said Jerry angrily. "One of these days he'll have a heart attack and die of fright."

Suey objected strongly to being left at home. He hated the boat but he hated being left still more; so before taking him out on any fishing trips which involved shooting the rapids, I used to dose him with aspirin till he was groggy.

The fact that we could now get in and out of the lagoon more frequently made fishing much more profitable. The lagoon had plenty of rock cod, but the salmon were all outside in the open sea.

Although our fishing activities did not commence till late in the season, we were still in time for the end of the herring run, and we found schools of them coming into shore with the flood tide. They provided us not only with food but with bait.

A special jigging-line was rigged up under Joel's instructions, and this we dropped over the side of the boat with a heavy weight attached to the end. A dozen or more hooks were tied on with yellow and red threads, and when we dropped it over the side of the boat we would see the backs of the fish swirling about below as they darted at the coloured threads. When the herring seized on the hooks, we hauled up the line dripping with fish. Half an hour's jigging usually covered the floor of the boat with herring.

We enjoyed our fishing expeditions, but hunting was another story. The need for fresh meat was always with us, but whenever we shot a grouse the sight of the blood-spattered feathers gave us a feeling of guilt. In consequence, most of our "hunting" was limited to killing tin cans perched on rocks.

In order to establish ourselves in the eyes of our neighbours as huntsmen, we sometimes put on a show for their benefit, and would casually announce that we intended to go deer-stalking early next morning.

For the supposed deer-stalk, we dressed up in rustly oilskin slickers and spent several hours crashing about in the bush yelling like Indians and firing haphazardly in all directions in order to create the impression that we were on the trail of game. The racket we made was further augmented by the squeals and barks of the dogs, who rushed insanely about in the underbrush. At a safe distance came the goats, bleating gently and nibbling at the tops of the spirea bushes. Bringing up the rear would be a long procession of clucking hens.

The result of this so-called hunt would be the complete exodus of every forest creature within a radius of several miles.

"How's the hunting?" inquired 'Lias one day with a wicked grin.

"Not so good," I answered with simulated regret. "Guess it's a bad season for deer, or something."

"How do you expect to carry a deer home if you kill one?" went on 'Lias.

"I don't know," I replied, feeling reasonably sure that we would never be faced with such a problem. "What *do* you do when you kill a deer?"

'Lias slowly rolled a neat cigarette, a process which I watched with feelings of corroding envy—mine always had strings hanging out of both ends and usually blew up when lit. I looked on in silence while he licked the paper.

"First," he said, "you take a rope and tie it round the back legs and then h'ist the beast up to the branch of a tree."

"Yes?"

"Then you take a knife and slit it open down the front."

"Yes?" faintly.

"Then you get right inside and take everything out," ended 'Lias airily, taking a step forward and embracing the air with outstretched arms.

"Oh," I exclaimed in tones of the utmost horror, "how awful! I couldn't do it."

'Lias lit his cigarette. "It's just like cleaning a chicken," he said.

Under his pitying and astonished eyes I had to admit shamefacedly that I had never cleaned a chicken.

"I suppose a person could cut a piece off it and bring it home," I said.

'Lias's face hardened. "Don't you let the fellers round here hear you say that," he answered. "That's what these hunters do. Me and Joel have been round after huntin' season and seen seven or eight deer shot down in a clearing and a quarter taken from each one, and the rest of the meat left to rot. I reckon that's what they call sport in the city."

"You and Joel hunt for sport," I ventured. "You even kill deer out of season."

'Lias's looked at me and his eyes had lost their kindly twinkle.

"Joel and me hunt for food," he said briefly.

Presently we gave up all pretext of hunting, and except for the fish lived mostly on canned meats and vegetables. Storage of fresh meat always presented a problem because of the lack of refrigeration. Our neighbours smoked and salted down quantities of fish and meat; butter and cheese were kept fresh by the unique method of digging deep holes in a damp patch of ground and sinking ten-gallon stone crocks in them. In these the butter could be kept for several weeks without going rancid.

The rocky nature of most of our property prevented us from digging storage pits anywhere near the house, but the shores of our little lake were full of these primitive refrigerators, the tops covered with boards and weighted down with stones to keep wild animals from helping themselves to our stores. The need for an extra half-pound of butter meant a mile climb up the rough hillside.

Having more spare time on our hands, we proceeded to explore the island. We climbed the bare cliffs, scrambled down into deep ravines and fought our way through dense bush in search of hidden lakes and abandoned logging sites.

The lakes, secreted in unsuspected valleys, always thrilled us with their primeval and unspoilt beauty. The mountains and trees reflected in their blue depths gave them a completely eerie look; gazing across the motionless water, we saw reflection melt into reality with no apparent break.

The abandoned dwellings which we occasionally came across had a different kind of loneliness. The owners long gone, the forest had crept up and gradually reclaimed its own, and the cabins were buried deep in trees and bush, doors and windows gone, and broken roofs falling in. Looking round the damp, sodden interior, we would see a broken chair or a rusty bed spring lying on the floor, a pair of mildewed jeans hanging dejectedly from a nail, or perhaps a pair of logging boots and some rusty traps.

Outside in the weedy remains of the garden, we sometimes found a few raspberry canes or a rose bush gone wild, mute evidence of the fact that once someone had tried to create something. Wondering about the unknown gardener, we walked away with an unaccountable feeling of sadness and left the humble dwelling to the strangling arms of the forest.

Our rambles often brought us out to the edge of the sea cliffs and sometimes resulted in exciting and unusual insights into the private lives of wild things. We were fascinated spectators at a battle between two mink, an affair of tangled brown bodies and gleaming teeth, accompanied by loud hisses and screams. We saw a family of sea otters diving and rolling their sleek bodies under and over a drifting log.

We gazed, round-eyed with wonder, at a school of blackfish on their slow unperturbed way north, every so often sounding and coming up again to spout geyser-like streams of water into the air. We saw an eagle attacked by a cloud of screeching herring gulls and watched the battle fought out against the pale-green evening sky until the eagle was driven down into the sea.

During the early part of the Indian summer, we found flowers growing in careless profusion among the grass and moss that carpeted the cleared spaces in the forest: straggling green monkey moss, blue gentian, maidenhair fern trembling in the spray of tumbling waterfalls, tiny scarlet toadstools, and clouds of pink seathrift waving in the wind on the cliff tops.

On one occasion we stumbled across an ancient Indian grave, a hollowed-out space beneath a great rock. Peering into the cavity we saw, besides the mouldering skeleton, the remains of an old war canoe, some cedar-bark cloth, and the remains of stone bowls and tools. We reached in and pulled out a stone pestle; and while we examined it, we thought about the past and wondered what manner of people these had been who had passed this way so long before us.

On hands and knees beside the ancient grave, I looked back across the vanished years and my imagination peopled the island again with its lost tribes. The smoke from their camp-fires rose again from the beaches, painted canoes thronged the bays and inlets, and ghostly moccasined feet padded through the forest.

With a little chill, I dropped the pestle and turned away, foreseeing a day when possibly some other race would find our ruined log house, and lying in the dust some of the things which we had treasured, and in their turn, perhaps wonder about us.

"It's such a beautiful world," I said, "I wonder why we have to die?"

"Better ask Vaino," answered Jerry lazily. "I bet he has all the answers pasted up on the ceiling."

October with its gipsy colourings had passed on, and we were well into November when the weather changed again. There was no immediate return of the great wind storms, but the grey skies hung low over the mountains, and the grey seas heaved drearily under the driving rain. We looked through the streaming windows at the dripping forest, and watched the last of the big scarlet-and-gold maple leaves trickle down through the bare branches and settle on the wet earth with a little dying whisper.

There were no more picnics and rambles in the woods. It took us all our time to saw up enough wood to keep the fires going.

The dogs huddled round the fire and refused to be dislodged. Terrible and Horrible lay outside on the doormat as close to the house as they could get; and the hens, moulting and bedraggled, drooped round the poultry yard, their eggs becoming fewer and fewer, until presently they ceased altogether.

"They don't look good at all," said Jerry, leaning over the fence. "Maybe they need a tonic or something."

I counted the flock.

"There's one missing," I said. "Something must have got it."

"Probably that grizzly of yours," sneered Jerry.

Ignoring her, I scurried into the chicken house and found the missing member of the flock crouched in a corner, heaving convulsive sighs, and with her crop distended in a most astounding manner.

"Jerry," I wailed in anguish, "come here quick!"

Jerry bounced into the chicken house and stooped over the bird. After some prodding and poking she made her diagnosis.

"Gas on the stomach."

"How about baking soda?" I asked.

"We'll try it. Bring her down to the house."

We soon found that baking soda as a remedy for whatever ailed the chicken was no remedy at all. It simply ran out of her beak and all over her tousled feathers.

"It's no use. She's going to die. I know she is," I cried in despair.

"I believe you're right," said Jerry, picking up the sufferer, "but we can't let her die without doing something. How about putting her in my bed and getting a hot-water bottle for her feet?"

The next few hours found us officiating at the death-bed, renewing hot-water bottles and hovering anxiously over a tattered purple comb and a beaky face, which was all that was visible above the blankets.

On inquiring of the poultry section in The Book, we found that it failed to provide any clue whatsoever as to the nature of the disease, although it devoted whole chapters to the desirability of electricity and running water in the hen houses.

"Next thing you know, they'll be advocating flush toilets," said Jerry, throwing down the volume in deep disgust. "Heat up some more water, this bottle is cold."

She bent solicitously over the bed. "Poor biddy, do you feel any better?"

Several hours later the convulsive struggles ended, and we sat dejectedly beside the corpse and mourned.

"This is the time when the hospital ship would have been really useful," said Jerry, rising at last, and taking up the lank corpse. "As it is, we shall never know what she died of."

The tale of the dying chicken spread among our friends, and lost nothing in the telling. The next mail day, Jerry and I found ourselves the centre of much good-humoured banter. Christian and Yonnie smiled at us shyly, their blue eyes twinkling with sly humour, and inquired if we were open for patients of other types.

The Dutchman pointed a stubby finger at us, shaking his long flaxen hair, and roared out in stentorian tones that he was surely coming in to see us as he had "wan dam goot bellyache bigosh."

The chickens continued to die off, victims of a variety of complaints which our neighbours vaguely suggested as being possibly "gapeworms," "tapeworms," "sour crop," or something which they diagnosed as the plain "pip."

We sought desperately for remedies, painting the throats of the possible gapeworm sufferers with a feather dipped in turpentine, and putting the sour-crop patients through a massaging process which Jerry called "draining their crank cases."

"Kill them all off," said Vaino with characteristic impatience. "They are getting too old to be of any use."

"How would *you* like to be killed when you are too old to be of any use?" I asked furiously.

"I would think it an excellent idea," replied Vaino coldly. "I am a firm believer in the humane disposal of all useless population, and if people nowadays weren't so awash in false sentimentality, they would see the sense of that for themselves. Why try to keep life in a body that would be better dead?"

"It's against my principles to take life," I said firmly.

"That is nothing but an excuse for selfishness," said Vaino, getting into his argumentative stride. "What you really dislike is the unpleasantness attached to the taking of life, so you invent principles and nobly let these wretched birds die a slow, miserable death."

"Oh, stop! Here we are, surrounded by sick and dying chickens, and all you do is come along with a lot of second-hand quotations."

Vaino looked angry.

"It's no use trying to interfere with the laws of nature. That's what is the matter with the world today. There are too many people in it who think they know better than Old Whiskers. Be practical, you can't operate with nothing but liabilities—just look at this."

He scooped up a tattered object that had strayed within reach of his long arms. Holding it up by the legs, he turned back what remained of the tail feathers and disclosed a rear end that appeared to have exploded.

"It looks as if had done nothing but lay square eggs all its life,

186

and it's going to die in a day or two anyway, so we'll kill it now and put it out of its misery."

With a quick movement he wrung the bird's neck and tossed the body aside.

I gave a screech of protest.

Taking me by the arm, Vaino led me down to the house. Outside the door, he paused to look approvingly at the woodpile, all neatly stacked—the chunks of fir dripping with streams of golden resin, the alder changing from its newly cut colour of dead white to deep orange, and the cedar, golden brown and richly perfumed.

"You do some things so well," he said, "much better than some of the men round here. None of the boys take time to stack a wood-pile properly."

"I like doing that," I said, "there's such a satisfaction in looking at a woodpile when you have cut every piece yourself. I just can't get used to killing things, though."

Vaino looked at me impatiently.

"You can't bear to kill things, but you don't mind eating the bodies that someone else has killed."

As usual, the underlying truth in his remarks reduced me to a state of irritated silence, and in the end it was Angus who solved our poultry problems and with considerably less talk.

Hearing from Blackie of the ruckus between Vaino and those two screwball women over the killing of a few old hens, he sailed into the lagoon one day, and with the rain beating down on his thin shoulders, rowed ashore in his dinghy bearing a crate filled with raucous young pullets from his own flock. Quietly he disposed of the few remaining hens in our poultry yard, cleaned out the house and installed the lively new-comers.

"Noo, ye wull soon be hae'in fresh eggs again," he said with his bashful smile.

"Oh Angus, how kind!" I said gratefully as I brewed a pot of tea for him. "I wish there was something we could do for you."

"Ye hae no been over to hear the gramophone lately," said Angus diffidently.

Jerry made a wry face behind his back.

"I know," I said, trying to stifle the proddings of my conscience, "the sea is so rough these days; but whatever happens Angus, we will surely come for Christmas."

Angus looked at us wistfully and said no more, and while I stirred my tea, I knew he was thinking of the times when the sea had not been rough, and when a little effort on our part would have brought him pleasure.

"I feel a selfish beast," I said after Angus had gone, hugging a loaf of home-made bread and comforted by the assurance that we would come to see him very soon. "We *must* go next week."

"I don't know where the time goes," said Jerry. "We always seem to be doing something."

And next week grew into the next month, and still there seemed to be no time to visit Angus.

The cold weather brought an endless chain of new tasks. The stoking of the fires and the constant sawing up of logs occupied a great part of the day. The livestock needed more attention, too. During the summer, the chickens and goats had roamed freely in the woods and except for a handful of grain or oats had found their own food. Now they had to be fed hot mash and there seemed to be an ever recurring array of buckets and pans to be scalded and washed—a loathsome task when every drop of water had to be carried by hand and heated in kettles on a wood stove.

The dogs, dripping from their walks in the rain, tracked mud and water through the house, and our former cursory dusting and sweeping now turned into a thoroughgoing daily house cleaning.

Two of the spaniels became infested with wood ticks, and Suey's overwhelming curiosity resulted in his being caught in a coon trap. On this occasion, my anguished shrieks for help as I watched his soft, furry body jerking convulsively in the trap brought all four Nelson brothers rowing frantically down the lagoon, their faces full of consternation. Behind them came a fishing boat, and as it drew in to shore, we saw Christian's bright golden head looking anxiously out of the pilot-house.

188

"Help! Help!" I screamed, driven to frenzy by Suey's agonized cries.

Christian and Joel rushed headlong up the beach.

"Where?" asked Joel, looking vainly around.

I pointed to the pitiful little heap of red fluff frantically trying to free a mangled paw from the steel trap.

"I can't open it. Get him out! Get him out!"

Joel gave me a half-comic look of disgust as Christian opened the trap which he had set earlier in the day and lifted a subdued and whimpering Pekinese into my arms.

"I told you not to bring that little beast to a place like this," said Jerry impatiently.

"Better you should keep him home while the trapping season is on," said Joel patiently.

"Why should I?" I retorted, turning on him furiously. "People have no right to set traps. There should be a law against it. I'll never wear a fur coat again as long as I live. I had no idea how a trapped animal suffers."

The men looked embarrassed and took refuge in their cigarette rolling. Christian, scarlet to his toes, threw his trap with a rattle of chains onto the deck of his boat and climbed unhappily aboard, while the rest of us returned to the beach in silence.

"After all," said Jerry in an angry aside, "the man has to make a living. You can't expect him to stop trapping just because of that damn dog of yours."

"He should make a living some other way," I said stubbornly.

For the next few days I carried Suey about with me constantly, and my mind dwelt persistently on all the wild things caught in traps and left to die.

"Sometimes they are chewing off their own feet to escape," said Sundi cruelly.

With the picture of Suey's agonized struggles before my eyes, and his screams of pain and terror ringing in my ears, I found myself listening for similar sounds, and began a persistent hunt for the coon and mink traps which were set along the shore. After I had sprung each one I found, they began to disappear and Christian's boat came into the lagoon no longer; but I knew that the trapping still went on in other parts of the island.

"The trappers visit their lines every day or so," said Joel easily. "The critters don't suffer much."

"How would *you* know?" I growled. "You aren't a critter."

On mail day, while waiting for the steamer in a drizzling rain, Christian kept aloof and watched me reproachfully from a distance.

"How's the trapping?" I said with a malicious smile.

For answer, he opened the hatch of his boat and lifted out three dead raccoons, stiff and cold, their little black feet held out piteously. Below in the hatch were a pile of mink, their pretty fur draggled and blood-stained, and their pain-filled eyes rigid and staring.

"How *can* you do it? Think how cruel it is," I said, turning away with a feeling of sickness.

"Women want furs," said Christian simply, laying the pathetic little bodies back in the hatch and closing the cover.

I turned again and met Vaino's dark sardonic gaze. "You will notice, it's *women* who want furs," he said.

"*I* don't—it's barbarous."

"Didn't you ever own a fur coat?" Vaino continued mercilessly.

Conscience-stricken, I was forced to admit that I had left two fur coats and a silver-fox scarf behind in the city.

"Somehow when I was buying them, I didn't think," I said sadly.

"That's the pity of it. People never do."

For a while there was a deadly silence. Jerry, sitting on the wet deck, was baiting her fishing-lines, preparatory to throwing them over the side. Vaino and Christian leaned against the side of the pilot-house with grim faces. Occasional shouts rose from the rocks where the fishermen were netting crabs.

I turned up my coat collar against the driving rain and tried to shake off an uncomfortable feeling of being in the wrong.

"You can say what you like," I persisted, "I still don't believe in killing things. I don't even like catching fish."

"You like eating them," said Jerry, rattling her fish spoons as she rubbed the polishing rag over them.

I looked distastefully at the barbed hooks.

"Let's try being vegetarians for a change, and live on cabbage and eggs and things."

"Every time you eat an egg you kill a potential chicken," said Vaino. "If you start thinking along those lines, you will find yourself ending up in a corner with a bale of hay. Let's just say that you don't believe in the unnecessary taking of life and let it go at that."

Unconvinced, I turned to the untangling of the fishing-lines; and as my chilled fingers unravelled the knots, I found myself meditating with increasing enthusiasm on the prospect of a dinner of fresh cod, stuffed with herbs and breadcrumbs, and surrounded by a buttery oyster sauce.

"I guess high ideals and an empty stomach don't go well together," I sighed.

Vaino's eyes glowed a little.

"That's the first sensible remark I have ever heard you make," he said.

Chapter 11

As THE rains ceased, the north-west wind cleared the skies and left the mountainsides white with a fresh powdering of snow. The days grew shorter and we saw less and less of the sun, until at last it never rose above the mountains that surrounded us, and we sank into a state of perpetual twilight.

As soon as the grey morning light glimmered through the windows we were up and out, sawing and splitting the wood for the fires, burning the last of the brush piles, and making the log house snug for the winter ahead.

We checked our storehouse supplies, making sure that in the case of prolonged storms we would not run out of food. We repaired the chicken- and goat-house roofs, making them waterproof for the livestock, and in the evening we sank deep into our comfortable chairs beside the crackling stove, and read.

The lagoon, in the grip of winter, took on a new wild beauty. At night, looking up from my book and seeing through the big windows the cold moon shining down on the rippling waters and the black outlines of the fir trees silhouetted against the night sky, I would heave deep sighs of pure pleasure.

We rarely ventured outside the lagoon now. Stern warnings from

Keijo regarding the dangers of trying to navigate a small boat through a Pacific gale had had no appreciable effect on us, but one or two first-hand experiences had convinced us that the sea in its evil moods was not a force to be treated lightly.

In all but the worst weather, the Nelsons went out to meet the mail steamer and brought in our mail along with their own. On the days when it was too rough for the steamer to stop, the mail sacks simply went back to town to wait for another week.

At intervals Vaino made brief appearances in the lagoon. He inspected our work and gave us much helpful advice. His incessant tirades on all manner of subjects, ranging from "Old Whiskers" to the state of civilization in general and the probable difference in taste between a brown egg and a white one, provided us with matter for many controversial discussions.

"I think you just talk for the sake of talking," I said one day, "and what's more, you are downright irreverent. Where do you expect to go when you die?"

"Nowhere," answered Vaino. "I shall be a disembodied ego wandering through space with a lot of other disembodied egos, and at last I will disintegrate and that will be the end of the Vaino you know."

"Don't you believe in an immortal soul?" I asked curiously.

"No-one has ever seen a soul. All anyone sees is an unhealthy physical body and a thoroughly unpleasant ego, and after the dissolution of those two there is nothing left that you would recognize."

"I rather like your unpleasant ego, Vaino," I said. "I'd hate to see it disintegrate."

Vaino's steely eyes softened a little.

"Now that's the nicest thing anyone has ever said to me."

On our next visit to Vaino's house, we found his theories on immortality pasted up, chapter and verse, over a crack in the wall.

"Cripes, what a guy!" sighed Jerry. "You never know whether it is he who is talking or somebody else."

Since the death of Fanny, Jerry had frequently cast envious eyes on Keijo's cattle and speculated on the price of canned milk as compared to the cost of feeding a cow.

My arguments about the lack of pastures and the high price of hay, plus the bother of milking and housing, had little or no effect.

"Think of the manure we would get for the garden," said Jerry.

"Think of the performance we had to go through when we milked Fanny," I argued back. "Take the comparative sizes of a goat and a cow, multiply by four, and see what kind of trouble you are in for."

But Jerry's dreams of owning a cow continued, and I waited in trepidation for the day when we would once again find ourselves burdened with some antiquated bag of bones, all horn, hoof and bad temper.

One chilly November day the ramshackle engines in Keijo's Monstrosity reached a state of disrepair to which his scanty engineering knowledge did not extend, and after vainly trying to rouse the smaller gas engine from the state of stupor into which it had fallen, he decided to take the whole business to town for a complete overhaul. Watching from the window we saw the Monstrosity anchored out in the lagoon and Keijo and Sundi rowing backwards and forwards with boatloads of gear and supplies, evidently preparing for several days' absence.

"I wonder if they are going to take Katie with them?" said Jerry.

The preparations for departure went on at intervals all morning, and Jerry and I, busy with our own chores, forgot about our neighbours until the familiar sound of a garbage can rolling downhill brought us down to the beach.

"They're off!" I said, looking at the green water churning round the lopsided propellers.

"They aren't," answered Jerry in ominous tones. "Here comes Keijo with trouble written all over him."

The Monstrosity had come to a screeching halt in front of our beach, and Keijo was rowing across in his dinghy in a determined fashion.

He strode up the beach and without preamble announced:

"You wanting cow—you milking mine while I away."

Jerry stared at him in dismay.

"You can't do that—I've never milked a cow."

"You have milking goats," replied Keijo, his bronzed features set in rigid lines.

"Ye-es, but that's different."

Keijo looked at her stonily, held up two fingers and said, "Goat." Adding two more fingers and clutching them together in a realistic bunch, he said, "Cow—both milking same way."

Disdaining further explanation, he gave us instructions on feeding, turned on his heel and departed, leaving us in a stunned silence.

We watched him sail out of the lagoon and then hurriedly rowed over to take stock.

Keijo's farm consisted of his house and a collection of dilapidated outbuildings. In addition to Katie and Sally, the two milk cows, we found that Keijo had neglected to mention his large, shaggy malemute, a thin, frightened cat and a dozen or so ragged hens. A cautious inspection of the pasture grounds revealed a playful young black bull which he had also neglected to mention.

"Oh I say—this is a bit thick," I complained. "A bull yet."

"It's only a young one," said Jerry; "it won't hurt you."

"It won't get the chance," I answered grimly.

As the mere thought of becoming familiar enough with a cow to be on milking terms with it caused a rash of goose pimples all over me, this task was by common consent assigned to Jerry, who being five inches taller and thirty pounds heavier was presumably more fitted for the job.

We looked at the cattle grazing placidly in the field. We inspected the chickens clucking contentedly in their yard. We attempted to console the malemute, who, lonely and bereft, was howling his heart out on the doorstep; and after looking vainly for the cat, who had fled at our approach, we rowed home to wait till the evening milking time came round.

At four o'clock we fed our own livestock and put them to bed for the night, then rowed across to Keijo's homestead to perform our new duties. As an insurance against accident I took along Suey and one of the spaniels; and for more reliable protection, I carried the .22.

The chickens had gone to roost. We filled up the mash hoppers and shut them up for the night.

The malemute, still wailing miserably, refused to be comforted with the venison bones which we fished out of a barrel in the barn, and the cat was still missing.

"I'll leave some milk out for her. I don't know what else I can do," said Jerry after a fruitless search. "Now for the cows!"

I gripped the gun firmly and felt for the extra shells in my coat pocket, called the dogs and followed her up the trail leading to the meadow.

"How are you going to get them down to the barn?" I asked.

"It's easy," replied Jerry with pretended nonchalance. "You just pick up a stick and shout 'Hep, hep!' and then they go. I've seen Keijo do it."

"Hep, hep!" I repeated thoughtfully as I patted the shells in my pocket. "I really don't believe it but I'm willing to be convinced."

On arriving at the meadow the first thing I did was to look for a large tree with branches low enough for me to climb into if necessary. Having found one, I settled comfortably down beneath it while Jerry found a stick and prepared for the roundup.

I watched while she marched onto the field, looked round and said "Hep, hep!"

The cows looked at her in round-eyed wonderment and went on placidly grazing.

"Hep, hep!" repeated Jerry, her voice rising a little, "Hep, hep!"

"Try it with a Finnish accent," I suggested, chuckling with glee. "Maybe they don't understand English."

Darting a look of black wrath at me, Jerry charged in among the cattle and brought her stick down with a resounding whack on Katie's rump.

"Holy mackerel!" I scrambled to my feet, my finger on the gun trigger. "She's coming right at me!"

For a brief second I was disagreeably conscious of the difference between the half-ton of beef-steak bearing down on me and the pound at a time I had always been used to seeing in the frying-pan, generally smothered with onions; then I lost my head and pressed the trigger.

The bullet whistled harmlessly up into the branches of the tree, and the dogs, all their inhibitions released by the shot, rushed shrieking onto the field, snapping at the heels of the cows, who lolloped helplessly backwards and forwards. The evening calm was shattered by barks, squeals, muffled moos and frantic shouts of "Hep!" while the young bull, all the play knocked out of him, straddled across the fence, bellowing mightily.

Feverishly I attempted to reload the gun and succeeded only in jamming the breech.

"Lord help us," I babbled to myself, "I never thought I'd die in a bullring."

Before I had succeeded in dislodging the shell from the gun, the uproar had subsided. Peering cautiously round the tree trunk, I saw Jerry holding both dogs down while she administered a thorough spanking. Katie, with an expression of utter bewilderment, had backed into a corner, while Sally was limping off to the barn followed by the young bull who, completely demoralized by the afternoon's events, had scrambled off the fence and hurried after her.

"Idiot!" Jerry marched across the pasture, snatched the gun out of my hands and thrust the struggling Pekinese into them instead. "Get yourself and these damn dogs out of here."

We reached the barn, Jerry driving the reluctant Katie by prodding her in the flanks with the gun barrel while I followed at a safe distance, dragging the disappointed dogs by their collars.

Sally and the bull were cowering in their stalls, completely subdued.

"Everything seems to be all right," said Jerry, giving Katie a final poke with the gun. "I'll feed them first, then do the milking."

Keijo's parting instructions had included a system of rationing that virtually required every straw to be counted.

"Just look how thin they are," said Jerry in pitying tones as she forked down the hay into the feed troughs. "For once I am going to see that they have a good meal; besides it will give them something else to think about while I do the milking."

The expected difficulties attached to cow milking failed to materialize, and the animals stood patiently and chewed their hay while Jerry experimented.

"This is easy," she exulted, "nothing to it at all. Oh boy, I'm surely going to buy me a cow."

The soft hissing sound of milk squirting into the pail and the breathing and snuffling of the cows was soothing after the late excitement, and I leaned contentedly against the door watching the light fade from the sky as the cold frosty night set in. On a rock outlined against the sky, the malemute sat with his nose pointed heavenward, howling mournfully, and around him the gnarled ancient apple trees assumed the fantastic outlines of dwarfs frozen in grotesque attitudes. A star twinkled above the ragged black mountain ranges and a still, numbing cold seeped through my heavy mackinaw coat.

"Hurry up," I said, poking my head round the barn door. "It's getting dark and I'm freezing."

Jerry came out carrying the milk pails.

"I've got to clean out the barn first," she said, setting the pails down and picking up a shovel. "Keijo said it had to be done every day."

I looked at the barn floor, swimming with liquid manure.

"Do you *have* to?"

"Of course, all barns have to be cleaned out," and Jerry went on to explain that each shovelful of refuse had to be thrown through a small hole in the wall of the barn onto the midden outside.

"If I miss that hole," said she, measuring it with her eye, "you are liable to be smothered in the backwash."

I pulled Suey's head out of the milk pail and retired to a discreet distance, from where I listened to the sound of metal scraping on cement, deep sighs, and a lot of succulent splashes. Then came a splash of another kind, a loud exclamation, and the rattle of a shovel falling.

"What happened?" I inquired, hurrying forward.

An irate and dripping object appeared in the doorway.

"If you're too stupid to guess, I'll tell you. That last shovelful really missed the target."

Not daring to risk further comment, I picked up the milk pails and led the way to the shed where the milk was separated, followed by a partner exuding an overpowering perfume which she described as "attar of cow."

In grim silence we washed and scalded the pails and set out the fresh milk; then, after fondling and trying to console the sad male-mute, we groped our way down to the float where our boat was moored.

Night had fallen and the shore-line was lost in an inky blackness. We guided our boat home by the light we had left burning in the window of the log house, shuddering a little as we heard the roar of the rapids and caught a glimpse of the white crests flashing in the blackness of the canyon.

Next morning Jerry, following Keijo's instructions, was up before it was light.

"What's the big idea?" I said sleepily. "It isn't time to get up yet."

"The cows have to be milked at six o'clock," answered a tired voice out of the gloom.

"Couldn't they wait till seven?"

"No! Cows have to be milked at regular hours or they blow up and burst."

"Hell's bells! Wouldn't *that* be something?"

"We'll have breakfast when we come back," said Jerry, "and for Pete's sake leave the gun and the dogs at home."

Now began a twice-daily pilgrimage across to Keijo's farm, feeding and milking the cows night and morning, driving them back and forth to the pasture, separating the milk, scalding the pans, and—to Jerry's unutterable dismay—constantly cleaning out the barn.

"I don't know how they do it," she sighed. "It doesn't seem to matter how much I take out at night, there always seems to be just as much next morning."

In fact the only bright spot in our cow herding was the large amount of fresh milk which we had at our disposal. Instead of the canned variety, we had buckets full of warm, frothy milk. We made butter, we poured cream over everything, and there was milk; everyone had milk—the chickens, the goats, the dogs and ourselves.

As the days passed, we began to long for Keijo's return. No amount of milk could compensate for the daily roundup in the meadow, the milking, the scalding of pans, the separating of milk, and the constant cleaning of the barn.

It was this latter task that proved to be the most disheartening, and Jerry's caustic comments on animals that seemed to be afflicted with chronic and profuse diarrhoea, coupled with her suggestions for remedying the matter by the use of plugs made out of Keijo's cork fishing floats, left me divided between mirth and anxiety.

In due course our sufferings were brought to an end by the return of Keijo. We watched the Monstrosity, clanking and exploding and apparently not a bit better for her overhaul, making her way into the lagoon, and presently Keijo rowed round the corner and came quietly ashore.

"Did you find everything all right?" asked Jerry anxiously.

Keijo looked at us with the faintest suggestion of a smile in his cold blue eyes.

"You still wanting cow?" he said.

Jerry put on an indifferent air.

"Not really," she replied. "You know, I've sort of got to like the taste of canned milk."

The activity caused by the preparations for winter died down, and a lull settled on the community. The nights were long and dark. The sea heaved restlessly and the wind snarled in crescendos round the house, making the darkness an eerie thing.

"What do you people usually do in the winter evenings?" we asked when Sundi was visiting us one day.

"We are going to bed," was the prompt answer.

"Ye gods! Don't you ever get tired of sleeping?"

"There is nothing else we can doing," replied Sundi with her hearty laugh.

Next, we tried the question on the Nelsons.

Joel looked at us in surprise.

"I dunno," he said, "there isn't anything to do. We go to bed early or just sit around."

"Wouldn't you think with all the time to spare, they would take up something? The study of Hindustani, or higher mathematics, or— or something?" said Jerry to me.

"Why don't *you* take up Hindustani?" I asked. "You have as much spare time as they have."

"Good idea," agreed Jerry enthusiastically. "We could get some books sent up and spend the winter learning languages."

Our good intentions came to nothing, the resolution to send for books was put off and put off, and we gradually began to find ourselves, like our neighbours, happily doing nothing.

The batteries on our radio set were running down and we had no spare ones. The set belonging to Joel and his brothers was broken, and the world could have collapsed without our knowing it; and even if we had known, I doubt if we would have cared.

"I never thought I could sit and think so much," said Jerry one evening.

"I know," I answered, "isn't it amazing? I have sat here every night for a week looking at that one pine tree outlined against the sky till I can almost tell you how many needles there on on the branches, and I am still not tired of looking at it; and the funny thing is that I am not a bit bored."

Lacking the excitement of major events, we found ourselves taking a passionate interest in the smallest occurrences. A new recipe for buns invented by Sundi gave us enough matter for several discussions. 'Lias's rug-making gave us another topic of conversation. He had unravelled an old white sweater and intended braiding the wool into a rug. The problem was, how to dye the skeins of wool different colours when there were no commercial dyes available.

Armed with information obtained from The Book, we had come to the rescue and our joint experiments had produced the most satisfactory results. Boiling one set of wool skeins in a solution of water and onion skins had changed them from a discoloured white to the most delicate shade of gold. Lichen had produced a beautiful shade of green. Beetroot turned another skein into a rich, glowing red and the juice from a jar of blueberries turned out a colour of purple that resembled heather. When completed, the rug was such a marvel of beauty and ingenuity that instead of laying it on the floor, the boys hung it on the wall.

At this time, we also built our last and permanent privy. We built it out of the planks we had rescued from the sea, and placed it in the privacy of the forest a long way from the house. Once again, it had no door, and at night looking out through the opening, one could see the light from our hurricane lantern reflected in the eyes of the forest animals, and they gleamed like tiny green fires in the dark.

"They keep you from feeling lonely," said Jerry.

The coming of the float-house into the lagoon was a different and more unpleasant event.

With the coming of winter, the logging camps up and down the coast had closed down and many of the float-house communities had broken up. Waiting out at sea for the mail, we had seen many of these floating villages being towed down the coast by sturdy tugs. There would be a cluster of individual houses standing on log booms, some with the families still in them, the smoke coming out of the stove-pipes and the children in their life-jackets playing out on the platforms that surrounded their dwellings.

We had asked questions: Would they return in the spring? Did the children go to school? Was it not dangerous for small tots to be running about with deep water all round?

The answers, as usual, were brief and lacking in detail, but we gathered that the loss of life among children was negligible; they practically slept in their life-jackets, and if one of the smaller ones fell into the sea, the life-jacket kept him afloat until someone came along and fished him out. Schooling was done by correspondence courses. When once a float-house community had broken up, it meant that the camp had closed down for good.

"What do they do then?" I asked.

"Go back to town and look for more work," was the answer.

The float-houses generally belonged to the logging companies, but now and then there was an individual who owned his own, and it was one of these that came floating into the lagoon behind a small and very much battered fishing boat. They came in late one afternoon when the early winter night was falling and anchored in the long shadows inside the entrance. Jerry and I did not realize that they were there until next morning when we were rowing down to the rapids on a clam-digging expedition.

On approaching the entrance, we were stunned with surprise at the sight of the shabby frame house resting on its platform of logs. The fishing boat was tied up to the end of one of the logs and the owner in his dinghy was busy making the float-house fast to the shore with cables.

The one-storey dwelling was in the last stages of dilapidation; the paint was peeling off its sides, the windows were cracked or broken and stuffed with sacks or covered with strips of cardboard. The tin stove-pipe was rusty and crooked.

Standing on the float watching the man was a depressed-looking woman, obviously and hideously pregnant, and gathered round her were five children ranging from a pale, thin boy of about twelve to a child still in arms.

We stared at the new-comers with that keen resentment known only to wilderness dwellers when they find their privacy invaded; and, the clam digging forgotten, we turned round and rowed back up the lagoon with all speed to spread the grim news that our quiet spot had visitors.

"They have no right to come in here," said Jerry indignantly to Joel. "They don't own any of the land."

"It's government land," said Joel. "Maybe they applied for a grant."

"I hope not," I said with a shudder. "You should just see the place they live in! I wouldn't keep a dog in it."

"Well, reckon they've as much right here as anyone," said Joel easily and continued with his work.

Keijo and Sundi were more in sympathy with our feelings, and the sight of the tumbledown home and the poverty-stricken family raised a resentment equal to ours.

Later in the day 'Lias rowed leisurely past our house with the ostensible purpose of setting cod lines outside the lagoon, actually to spy out the situation for himself. A few words in passing with the owner of the float-house gave him the information that the invasion was a temporary one. The man of the house had merely anchored his family in the lagoon while he looked for work in another camp, and intended returning for them in a few weeks. That same day he went away in his boat, leaving the woman and her children alone in their floating home.

Except for the rare occasions when we went out of the lagoon, we never saw them. Although the dinghy had been left tied up to the logs, they never seemed to use it and apparently were content to stay in the house or on the platform on which it rested.

"What will they do when they want supplies?" we asked Joel.

"They've probably got plenty of beans and canned stuff to last them awhile," replied Joel.

"I wonder where they get their water?" said Jerry curiously.

"There's an old quarry hole back up the mountain. I saw the eldest kid rowing ashore with buckets and climbing up there the other day."

As time passed and there was no sign of the father returning, another matter began to worry us.

"Suppose that woman decides to have her baby some dark night?" I said to Sundi. "What a mess! No doctor or nurse or phone. I suppose we shall all have to pitch in and help."

For once Sundi was not co-operative.

"I am not knowing anyt'ing about babies," she said decisively. "I am not helping. *He* not liking it."

"Neither do I know anything about babies," said Jerry indignantly. "In all the books I have read where anyone has a baby, everyone rushes about boiling water, but nobody ever says what they do with it."

"I watched a cat having kittens once," I said meditatively. "She didn't seem to need any water. She sure used up lots of spit, though."

In the meantime we all went about our business. The woman and her children kept close to their ramshackle home and made no move to approach us. Rowing past one day, I tried a tentative wave of my hand to the four younger children playing on the logs above the deep, fast-running water—a gesture that immediately sent them scurrying into the house like small, frightened animals.

"If they need help, I suppose they will ask for it," I said shrugging my shoulders.

Then one cold, windy day the husband returned.

For two or three days we had seen no sign of the woman and the eldest boy, although the younger children in their life-jackets still played on the logs.

Jerry and I, fishing for cod out in the centre of the lagoon, saw the fishing boat, like a fussy little hen, back up to the float. The elder boy came out of the house, took the mooring rope and made it fast to the logs, after which he and his father went into the shabby home. In a little while we saw the father come out again, untie the mooring rope, climb aboard his boat and set off to the far end of the lagoon where the four brothers lived.

The pale, thin boy shooed the children inside and jumping into the dinghy commenced loosening the cables that held the float-house to the shore.

"Thank goodness, they are going," said Jerry, watching with relief. "I haven't been able to sleep nights waiting for that emergency call."

Half an hour later the fishing boat returned. The towing lines were fixed to the boom and the family sailed out to sea, as complete strangers to us as they had been on the day of their arrival.

"Let's go down and dig clams," said Jerry later in the day. "I haven't been able to enjoy a good clambake since that bunch of gipsies arrived. I couldn't fancy digging clams with that row of eyes fixed on me."

We beached our boat on a patch of gravel just inside the entrance and while the rapids roared a few yards away, we enthusiastically dug for clams with a sense of freedom we had not known since the arrival of the strangers.

When we returned we found Joel and 'Lias waiting for us.

"Clams!" we said exuberantly. "First chance we've had since those squatters arrived."

"Yup! Reckon they won't bother you no more," said Joel, following us into the house.

Jerry sluiced fresh water over the clams and set them on the stove to steam.

"Just about got out of here in time, I'd say; that woman could have had her baby any minute, right here in the lagoon."

"Yup," answered Joel with an impassive face, "that's just what she did."

"*What?*" I turned an incredulous face towards him. "You mean she actually *had* it?"

"Tell 'em, 'Lias," said Joel, rolling himself a cigarette.

From 'Lias the story came out in bits.

The woman had had the baby three days before her husband had arrived, alone and with no-one to help but the twelve-year-old boy. Afterwards, the whole responsibility of the household had rested on his thin, childish shoulders—the nursing of his mother, the care of the younger children, the collecting of the wet wood which was all they had to use in their stove, the preparing of the meagre meals and the dragging of the water buckets from the quarry hole in the mountain.

The return of the father had found them without milk for the children, and the trip up to see the Nelsons had been to buy a few

206

cans of condensed milk to help them out until he could tow his family to more hospitable quarters.

"Oh, I feel so ashamed!" I said. "But why didn't they tell us? You know we would have done anything we could."

"Guess they were too proud to ask," said Joel, toying with his cigarette. "Guess it was up to us to offer."

"We couldn't," I said indignantly. "You can't very well go calling on perfect strangers and ask them if they have enough to eat and when they are going to have a baby."

There was a silence while Joel went through a difficult and ponderous thought process.

"Reckon you could have asked them if they had everything they needed," he said at last.

"*We* could have asked?" I said. "Why didn't *you* ask?"

"Guess it's a woman's job," said Joel imperturbably.

"I don't see that at all. After all, we are practically new-comers here and we can't be expected to know the rules of etiquette that apply to these parts."

Joel and 'Lias made no reply.

"Keijo and Sundi should have done something," said Jerry.

"You couldn't expect it of them," answered Joel, getting up to go. "They don't know no better."

With that they took their departure, disapproval written all over their tanned faces.

Smarting under Joel's criticism, Jerry and I looked at each other helplessly, and as soon as we could, we sought out Vaino and told him about the incident.

"The days of leaving calling-cards on new-comers are over," said Jerry. "Even in the city you don't do that."

"You are not in the city now," said Vaino sharply. "In a place like this people depend on their neighbours. Think how many times the boys have helped you. Joel was quite right, it was up to you to offer help if it was needed. You are quite intelligent enough to know how to do it tactfully."

"But suppose she had sent word for us to come and help when

the baby was born?" I said in a panic. "What on earth would we have done?"

Vaino gave me an eloquent look.

"Just what that twelve-year-old boy did," he said quietly. "Anyone with any common sense can do *something* at a time like that."

Not feeling so sure of my capabilities of dealing with such a situation, I still flushed with shame at what seemed unusually severe criticism.

"Another time I will know better," I said soberly.

"Another time!" repeated Vaino impatiently; then, looking at our crestfallen faces, he said a little sadly: "Another time? Have you ever noticed how seldom there *is* another time?"

Chapter 12

THIS LATEST episode, combined with Vaino's criticism of what he evidently considered to be our shortcomings, left us considerably depressed; and then one day, Joel and his brothers invited us to go with them to a dance.

"A dance?" exclaimed Jerry to the most loquacious of the four, who had been charged with delivering the invitation. "Do you have dances here?"

The dance, it appeared, was to take place at the home of Big Pete, the handsome half-breed, who, possessing a large family, possessed also the largest house on the island.

"Who's going?" inquired Jerry cautiously.

"Oh, everybody goes," replied 'Lias, rolling himself a cigarette.

"What do they wear?" I asked, looking down at my ragged slacks.

"Oh—dresses and things."

"What sort of dresses?" I persisted, wishing that information was not so hard to extract.

There was a pause, a vague look, and then a valiant plunge into uncharted depths.

"Muslin, I guess."

"*Muslin!*" I exclaimed in horror. "Holy cow!"

'Lias gazed wildly round for inspiration, and his eye, falling on the flowered window curtains, lit up with a gleam of hope.

"Something like that," he said, fingering the gay material.

"I have never worn anything like *that* in all my life," declared Jerry positively.

'Lias lapsed into his habitual silence and looked unhappy.

Jerry and I looked across at each other dubiously.

She raised her eyebrows in mute inquiry, and after a moment's hesitation, I nodded, and the invitation was accepted.

The dance was scheduled to take place that night, and as soon as 'Lias had left, we immediately set about making ourselves presentable for our début into island society.

The household scissors, which had been used for everything from clipping the dogs to cutting wire, were brought into action, and we each took a turn at barbering; then our mutilated locks were washed and patted into some semblance of order.

Surplus finger nail was hacked off and sandpapered down. The galvanized wash-tub was filled with hot water and a thorough scrubbing followed. Then from forgotten wardrobe trunks we proceeded to unpack garments which we considered to be suitable for the occasion.

Not being able to raise anything in the least resembling chintz or muslin, Jerry chose a navy-blue tailored suit and a white silk shirt, while I picked out a dress of rust-coloured crêpe that I had saved from my former city wardrobe as being too good to part with.

"It is so plain that no-one will ever guess how much it cost," I said, surveying myself by inches in a small hand mirror.

Sheer silk stockings and rust-coloured suede shoes with four-inch heels completed my ensemble. Arrayed thus, we hoped we would not be too conspicuous among a chintz-and-muslin-clad throng.

While Jerry dived down into the bottom of a trunk in search of suitable wraps, I checked the strings of my violin, which had been invited to the dance along with its owner.

At six o'clock, a busy chugging and snorting off the beach announced the arrival of the fishing boat belonging to our escorts, and a few minutes later two of them rowed ashore in the dinghy and appeared at the door, their faces outrivalling ours in cleanliness and shine, and their khaki shirts and trousers crackling with starch.

Six o'clock seemed a little early for a dance, but the brothers, questioned on the subject, spoke of having other places to call at first. They had to pick up the Dutchman and his "woman," also some "likker."

We said good-bye to the dogs, checked the fires, made sure the goats were fastened up, and accompanied the men back to their boat. We climbed onto the fishing boat, the dinghy was hauled aboard, and after the customary session of cursing and tinkering, the engine started and the journey commenced.

After an hour's sailing in a choppy sea, we arrived at the Dutchman's homestead, where we all disembarked at a somewhat tipsy wharf and groped our way by lantern light up a thickly wooded hillside.

My silk stockings were snagged by brambles and my progress was considerably impeded by my thin spike seels, which kept sinking into the boggy soil and anchoring me to earth.

The brothers, completely confounded by the combination of an imported gown and a pair of stilt-like heels, suddenly became very solicitous as to my welfare, and stayed behind to help me over the rough spots, to my great amusement. Up to now, my standard costume of tattered slacks and broken-down running-shoes had aroused no particular interest among the masculine population, but I soon found that a French dress and a touch of lipstick brought about a complete reversal of feeling, and the men vied with each other in their attentions.

Assisted by our overly attentive escorts, we arrived at the house and were greeted by the Dutchman's uproarious shouts.

"You coom right in—haff a drink—haff a chair. Vare iss my voman? LOO-EE! Vare iss you?"

We sat down and looked round us. The one-room dwelling was

clean and bare, with the simplest of home-made furnishings. The bed was made of a wooden frame supported on four blocks of stove-wood and covered with chicken wire. The mattress lay on top of this and had several layers of thin, well-patched blankets over it. The curtains were made of flour sacks, washed and bleached, according to the usual custom of the islanders, who never wasted anything. There was a wooden table, some kitchen chairs and a big cook-stove. Two or three apple boxes nailed to the walls served as cupboards for the few dishes and cooking utensils, and under the small window stood a bench holding three buckets of well water. A row of nails on the wall held a few garments and a large wolfskin served as a rug. The place, like most of the island's homes, was strictly utilitarian and gave a peculiar impression of impermanence.

For the next hour or two Jerry and I sat on the hard wooden chairs, and while the men made frequent trips into the woods to inspect the Dutchman's private distillery, we tried to make conversation with his "woman," a tired, sorrowful-looking creature who kept casting sidelong glances at my dress and high heels, and seemed to be too beaten by life to have any ideas left.

"Have you lived here long?" asked Jerry, looking round the bare room.

"Four year—maybe a bit longer—I don't know," she answered with a slight shrug of her shoulders.

"It must be lonely for you when your—er, when Hans is away fishing," I said. "Have you any family?"

"We had a baby once—it died. I was alone and there was no doctor."

"Couldn't anyone get to you?" I asked, appalled.

"Winter time—too rough," was the short reply.

I thought of the woman in the float-house.

"Life isn't very easy for women in these places, is it?" I said, looking at her haggard face.

She looked once again at my dress and the smart wool coat thrown over the back of the chair.

"I had a dress that colour once," she said in dull tones.

I moved uncomfortably on my hard chair and it was with a feeling of distinct relief that I saw the men appear in the doorway, shouldering a small cask which dripped a revolting-looking liquid with a smell faintly reminiscent of varnish.

There was a suspicious brightness in their eyes, and the Dutchman's laugh was unusually strident.

"Come on—time we were moving," said one of the men, grasping my arm.

We ploughed back through the mud to the wharf, an incongruous group—Jerry and I in our citified attire, Joel and Blackie jealously guarding the cask, and the Dutchman, bundled up in a plaid mackinaw coat and battered sou'wester, followed dumbly by his woman, a thin mackintosh pulled over her cotton dress and her feet encased in heavy knee-high rubber boots.

"Whee-ee-ee, we're off to the races!" cried Jerry exuberantly, tramping over the gravel. "Oh my hat, just look at the float!"

I looked, and groaned in dismay. The float was well awash with the rising tide and a wide stretch of water lay between it and the shore.

"I'm staying right here till the tide goes out," I said with great determination. "If you think I'm going to swim in these clothes, you're very much mistaken."

The Dutchman gave a delighted roar of laughter and picking up a plank, proceeded to use it to bridge the gap between the float and the shore.

"You giff me your handt and I pooll," he shouted. "My voman, she coom behindt and poosh."

A precarious and undignified crossing was thus effected, but by the time I had boarded the fishing boat, my feet were thoroughly and most uncomfortably soaked.

"Serves me right," I grumbled, scraping the mud and broken clam shell off the heels of my shoes. "I suppose all the other guests will be wearing oilskins and gumboots."

Joel and Blackie lifted the cask aboard and kicked the engine into action, and we started off again.

When we drew near our destination, we began to see lights twinkling over the water from the windows of a large house built on a rocky promontory. On the sea below it, coming from all directions, were the red and green riding-lights of fishing boats, loaded with guests, all bound for the festivities. Shouts of greeting echoed across the water, and there were the familiar sounds of clanking anchor chains and the soft swish of oars.

The one-eyed Swede in his leaky row-boat came up beside us, and leered up with his good eye.

"Where's the dance?" I asked, leaning over the side.

"She bane right dar," pointing to the lighted house.

I turned as a loud splash came from the bow of the boat, and saw 'Lias and Joel lowering the anchor. Blackie and Sonny dropped the dinghy from the deck into the sea, and the gunwales sank dangerously close to the water as we all crowded into it.

We rowed ashore and, scrambling over rocks slippery with seaweed, made our way up to the house.

The front door was wide open and led into one large room.

Not a vestige of furniture was there, nothing but wooden benches ranged round walls which were covered with hideous flowered paper, badly torn in spots.

The general effect was rendered even more ghastly by the greenish glare of a single gasoline lamp which hung hissing from the ceiling.

About a dozen half-breeds were sitting on the benches, dressed in cheap navy-blue suits and highly polished brown boots, their jet-black hair plastered close to their heads with strongly scented brilliantine.

I hesitated on the doorstep as I met their beady black eyes, and meditated a quick get-away back to the fishing boat; but before I could make up my mind, a firm hand in the middle of my back pushed me forward, and a voice behind me murmured, "Here's Pete."

Looking up I saw Big Pete, very handsome and dignified, coming towards us accompanied by his wife, a full-blooded Indian.

214

"We are proud to have you in our home," said Big Pete, and the dingy room might have been a palace.

I held out my hand, and the Indian took it hesitantly. It was a greeting with which she seemed to be unfamiliar, and we looked at each other curiously.

I saw a tall, proud woman dressed in a flowered gingham garment, grey lisle stockings, and strong black shoes. Her hair, crow black and shiny as satin, hung down in two tight braids over her shoulders. While she spoke, I found myself regretting the substitution of such a hideous example of civilized dress for the picturesque native costume.

"You will please to follow me," she said with dignity, and turning away she led us into a small room opening off the main room where she invited us to remove our wraps. This room was also bare of furniture except for a couple of camp cots, on which two or three Indian babies snored peacefully.

We hung our coats on one of the nails hammered into the bare wooden walls and after looking askance at the dark little faces resting on the pillows, followed our hostess back to the main room, anxious to rejoin our escorts, who, we were beginning to feel, were our last link with civilization.

Apparently it was not the custom for the women to mingle with the men until the actual dancing started, for our hostess led us through the guests and into still another room.

This room was in complete darkness, the supply of lamps having seemingly given out; and it also appeared to be full of people, judging by the heavy breathing which seemed to come from all sides. What light there was, filtered through the open door from the gasoline lamp hanging outside, and as my eyes became accustomed to the gloom, I saw that we were in a kitchen. I also realized that the breathing came from a row of Indian women seated on a long bench and solemnly watching me.

Looking at them more closely, I saw that 'Lias had been completely wrong in his chintz-and-muslin prophecies. The older women, like their hostess, wore print house dresses, cotton stockings and black leather shoes, while the younger girls were wearing cheap mail-order skirts and blouses—blouses made of imitation satin in the most vivid of pinks and blues. Chalky white powder was plastered thick over each dusky glowing face, finishing abruptly at the chin. Lips were smeared thick with rouge and there was an overwhelming odour of cheap perfume. The only natural things about them were their beautiful teeth and flashing black eyes.

Jerry sniffed the air pointedly. "Smells like a third-rate whorehouse," she said.

I giggled nervously. "How would you know?" I asked, looking round me unhappily. "I grew up in the belief that Indians wore feathers. Never since I came to this country have I seen an Indian with any more feathers than a grasshopper."

"They would look a lot more attractive in feathers if they only realized it," mumbled Jerry, holding her handkerchief to her nose.

Introductions followed, and I bowed to the dark Indian faces—the seamed, stolid countenances of the older women and the smiling beauty of the young ones.

Outside, the noise of fresh guests arriving and the sound of laughter and scraping feet floated through the open doorway, and added to this came the sound of instruments tuning.

Peering out of the doorway to catch a glimpse of the orchestra, I saw two loggers clad in violently coloured plaid shirts, their blue Levis kept from falling over their slim hips by broad brass-studded belts of cowhide. One of them was strumming softly on a guitar, while the other, with an absorbed expression, was tuning a banjo. The third member of the group was a young breed who was drawing feeble squeaks from a fiddle held close to his stomach and a bow gripped round the middle of the stick.

While I watched, they swung into action, and in a minute all was turmoil. Men dashed into the kitchen, grabbed partners indiscriminately and hurled themselves wholeheartedly into the dance.

'Lias pulled Jerry out onto the dance floor and Joel rescued me from a circle of dark, unsmiling half-breeds and led me into the middle of the melee. I found myself swallowed up in a bearlike hug

216

and swung around the room. Sometimes I rode on my partner's feet, sometimes he rode on mine. Under this treatment my salt-stained shoes collapsed completely. One spike heel snapped in half and Joel caught me by the arm as I lurched sideways.

"That's the end of my dancing," I said thankfully. "Will it be all right if I take my fiddle and play with the orchestra?"

"Reckon they'd be right pleased to have you," replied Joel.

Limping back to the kitchen, I unwrapped my violin and went over to join the other players.

The addition of a complete stranger to their ranks did not appear to surprise them at all. They greeted me with smiles that showed every strong white tooth and moved further up the bench to make room for me.

"Another violin—that's swell! What pieces can you play?"

"I'll follow you," I said confidently. "Just play anything you like."

They looked at me with respect and I tucked my violin under my chin and prepared to tune.

"Give me A," I said, turning to the other fiddler, who was watching me with open mouth.

The banjo player laughed.

"He doesn't know the names of the strings," he said giving a loud metallic plonk on his own instrument.

"How does he tune then?" I asked, bewildered.

"He doesn't! He just slides around till he finds the note."

"I'm sure it would sound better if you were all tuned to the same pitch," I said, feeling slightly dazed.

It was the banjoist who looked dazed now.

"Pitch?" he answered vaguely. "Pitch? Aw shucks, we don't bother with that kind of stuff—we just play."

He picked up his banjo.

"C'mon boys, let's go."

I watched them helplessly. Both players had their heads stuck out at an identical angle, and the right foot of each beat out the time with a heavily calked logging-boot.

The racket produced by this combination of plucking and stamping was deafening and all semblance to tune was completely absent, but there was rhythm of a sort.

I looked at the other violinist to see what he was doing, but he was apparently so overcome at finding himself in the presence of someone who talked familiarly about pitch that he sat there goggling at me with his fiddle drooping between his knees.

"What are they playing?" I asked.

No answer. Only a round-eyed stare of wonderment.

I looked again at the others and catching a bar or two that sounded vaguely familiar, I decided that the tune they were tormenting was "Tavern in the Town"; and picking up my violin, I joined in with energy.

After a few bars, the other two stopped and looked at me suspiciously.

"What are *you* playing?" asked one.

"'A Tavern in the Town,'" I replied uneasily. "Isn't that right?"

They looked at me with pity.

"*We're* playing 'Ragtime Cowboy Joe.'"

"Does it really matter?" I said sulkily, wiping away the surplus rosin from under the bridge of my violin.

The banjo player looked astonished.

"Guess you've never played in orchestras before?"

"Once or twice," I admitted feebly, "symphony orchestras."

"Oh yes," he answered loftily, "that's different. *This* kind of thing takes practice." Then, lifting a ham-like hand, he gave me a slap between my shoulders that made my eyes bulge and my teeth rattle. "Never mind, you'll get onto it in time."

All the superiority knocked out of me along with my breath, I requested humbly that they mention the name of the tune before they played it, and after this things went along better.

The music was made up of tunes belonging to the "Little Brown Jug" and "Camptown Races" vintage, and was played at a tempo calculated to wear down all but the hardiest and most enthusiastic of dancers. I played along valiantly and was gratified when my efforts drew smiles of approval from my partners.

"That's swell!" nodded the banjoist, wiping his forehead. "Guess you must have taken lessons some time, eh?"

The half-breed fiddler, now recovered from his shyness, moved closer to me, and with that freemasonry that exists between all string players, we began comparing violins and bows. I loosened the hairs of his bow, the stick of which was bent into a perfect arc. I also showed him how to tune his violin.

The room by now was full of sweating people. All the mail-day group had arrived, and there were Indians and whites and half-breeds rollicking around together in the highest spirits. The blond Scandinavians, towering head and shoulders above the others, stalked among the crowd, their blue eyes glassy with drink. Indian babies were rolling about on the floor and being tripped over by the dancers, and a typical Indian mongrel dog kept wandering sociably about among the guests, until thrown unceremoniously out of the front door, from which he promptly found his way round the house and made a re-entry through the back door.

In the kitchen an improvised bar was working overtime, and raucous laughter rang out from a distant corner where the Dutchman, surrounded by his special cronies, was sitting on his cask.

The full-blooded Indians maintained a solemn and unsmiling dignity throughout, their fierce black eyes inscrutable and a panther-like grace in their movements that even their cheap ready-made suits could not hide. Some of the half-breeds, however, were falling by the wayside. Big Pete, in his shirt-sleeves and with his hat on the back of his head, was having a busy time scraping up the dead and dying and dragging them outside.

During one of the all too brief pauses, the guitar player, who had been constantly refreshing himself with long draughts from a flask kept in his hip pocket, invited me to step outside and have a drink.

"Where is it?" I asked warily.

"On my boat."

I looked about me. Judging by the effect the liquor was having on some of the dancers, it seemed to have more than usual potency. I glanced sideways at my swaying fellow musician and hesitated, overcome by an unusual feeling of caution. After all, a drink in a parked car was one thing, but a drink in a parked fishing boat was entirely out of my range of experience.

"Thanks awfully," I said; "if you don't mind, I'll wait and have one later on."

The dance roared on.

The guests whirled past us with ear-splitting yells. The Nelson brothers, their long legs flying and their once carefully combed hair falling in wild elf locks over their eyes, pranced past us, each with a giggling half-breed girl on his arm.

I caught sight of Jerry dancing with the Irish postmaster, whose ten-gallon hat had settled down over his eyes, and who was blindly and doggedly guiding her round and stamping all over her feet at the same time.

"How about a nice dreamy waltz?" he begged as he swayed past.

My partners came to the end of their stock of pieces and started all over again. There was only the shortest of breaks between the dances. One ran into another.

The other violinist deserted us and went to mingle with the dancers, and presently we saw Big Pete dragging him out by the heels.

"They sure can't take that kickapoo juice," grinned the banjoist.

The Indian babies were gradually gathered up and put to bed on piles of coats under the benches, where they slept peacefully, oblivious of the battle raging round them.

The dog was still being thrown out of the front door and was as persistently coming in at the back, and the Irishman's demands for a "nice dreamy waltz" were becoming more and more violent.

"How long do these dances last?" I asked, resting my aching bow arm on my knee.

"Three days sometimes," answered the banjoist.

"Holy cow!"

I looked round for Jerry, anxious to impart this startling piece of information, and located her backed into a corner, where she was warding off the determined efforts of the Irishman to drag her onto the dance floor again.

"I'm too tired, Pat," I heard her say.

The Irishman looked helplessly around, and, his glassy eye falling on the Dutchman's cask, he staggered over to it, helped himself liberally, then swayed back to Jerry with outstretched arms.

"*Now* you feel better," he said.

"Say—this is quite a brawl, isn't it?" I said, watching the scene with wide eyes. "Do you have affairs like this often?"

The banjoist smiled. "Not as often as we would like—only when someone is going away."

"Who's going away?" I asked, looking round curiously.

It appeared then that the party was being given for Big Pete himself, who was going into the mountains after big game with a hunting party and expected to be away for some time.

I looked at Big Pete hauling a prostrate half-breed off the floor, the dancers skimming past him.

"*He* doesn't seem to be having much fun," I said.

"No—but everybody else is," came the quick reply.

About three in the morning, there was a breathing-space while refreshments were served. I laid aside my violin with a sigh of relief.

The refreshments had been provided by the guests themselves, each person having contributed something in the nature of cake or sandwiches.

Big Pete, still with his hat on the back of his head, tore himself away from the job of collecting corpses and carried in a large washbasket full of hot dogs, while small Indian girls passed round steaming mugs of coffee and plates of gaudily iced cake.

While the dust settled back on the floor and the dancers rested their feet, I drank two cups of watery coffee in order to relieve a head which was beginning to buzz in an alarming manner, and watched the antics of the guitar player, who was emptying the contents of the sugar bowl over his guitar and trying to feed hot dogs to the banjo.

221

"Oh no you don't!" I said, disentangling my violin from the necklace of sausages which he was draping round it.

"It'sh hungry too," he said with a liquory grin; "it'sh been working hard."

"It's on a diet," I said firmly, laying the instrument out of reach.

The banging together of two pan lids and the voice of a man calling loudly for order caused a diversion, and someone got up and announced that we were to be favoured with a song from our hostess.

I looked up, half hoping to hear her sing a native song in her own language, and was conscious of a keen sense of disappointment when she piped up with "My Blue Heaven," sung in a thin, wailing soprano and with that peculiar off-key intonation common to Indians.

After the applause had died down, the same man got up and said that we would now have a violin solo.

I looked round.

"That's you," said the banjoist, smiling encouragingly.

While wiping the traces of sugar and grease off my unfortunate fiddle, I ran mentally through my repertoire of violin solos, and wondered how a Beethoven sonata would sound without the piano and what the effect on the audience would be.

I looked questioningly at my partner.

"What shall I play?" I asked.

" 'Danny Boy,' " he answered, strumming a few chords on the banjo.

So Danny Boy was thrown to the wolves, complete with ragtime banjo accompaniment.

Never was an audience less critical. Claps, stamps and frenzied whoops followed the last notes, accompanied by hearty thumpings on the cask by the Dutchman. As I bowed acknowledgement, one of the Indians leaped out to the middle of the floor with a bone-chilling yell, glared round for a minute with glittering eyes, and then, throwing back his head and shaking loose his greasy black

222

hair, broke into a native dance, jumping up and down with stiff legs and savagely grinning teeth.

In a minute Big Pete and two or three of the other men had hustled him out of the room.

"Is he drunk?" I whispered to the banjoist.

"No. They get like that sometimes, the dancing excites them," he said indifferently. "Guess we'd better start playing again."

He dug his elbow into the ribs of his partner, who was nodding and swaying over his coffee cup.

"Sober up, pal," he said, "we've got a long way to go yet."

The guitar player came to with a start, pushed the rest of his half-eaten hot dog into his mouth, and picking up his guitar, mumbled, "Okay, le's go."

The party was on again.

In a state of exhaustion, I excused myself and retired to the cool darkness of the kitchen. Jerry, seeing me go and taking advantage of the Irishman's preoccupation with the cask, followed me and we picked our way over the prostrate forms lying like felled trees on the kitchen floor.

"Hullo—look who's here," said Jerry, poking at one unconscious body with the tip of her shoe.

I bent over the giant frame and peered into the flushed, bloated face.

"Why—it's Christian!"

"Doesn't he look frightful?" said Jerry in disgust, "just like a beetroot with apoplexy. No-one would think he was handsome if they saw him now."

"Well," said I, clutching my head with both hands, "if he has a headache at least he doesn't know it. For goodness' sake let's sit down before I fall down."

Sitting in the semi-dark, we watched the dancers charge noisily past the doorway and the staggering Irishman searching vainly for his lost partner.

Men kept walking past us to a dark corner in the rear where a mysterious business involving much bubbling of liquids and clinking of bottles was being transacted. On their return, amazingly revitalized, they stopped and asked us to dance. Jerry, shaking her head, made excuses and they wandered away with regretful murmurs.

"I wonder if that snake juice is fit to drink?" I said after a while. "My head is aching so hard it feels as if it would bounce off my shoulders."

A tall figure immediately materialized out of the gloom.

"May I get you a drink?" asked a voice; and turning my head, I saw Yonnie, the Icelander, bowing politely to me.

"What have you got?" inquired Jerry suspiciously, no doubt recalling the dubious contents of the Dutchman's cask.

"Anything you say," was the smiling answer.

"How about rum? That's pretty safe," said Jerry to me. "It might do your head good."

"Yess we haff rum," said Yonnie. "A leetle rum cock's tail perhaps?"

"That will do fine," I said, "and let's find a quiet place to drink it."

Threading our way through the dancers, we sought refuge in the room where our coats were hanging. I appropriated the only chair, and Jerry and Yonnie sat down on an Indian baby which was asleep in a camp cot, covered with tarpaulin coats and fish oil.

Uncorking the bottle, Yonnie poured a little of its contents into a cracked and handleless teacup, and with a charming smile and a courteous bow, handed it to me. One sip of the alleged "cock's tail" and I gasped vainly for breath. Not only my headache, but my whole head seemed to vanish. I handed the cup to Jerry and wiped my streaming eyes.

"Cripes—I'm poisoned!" I croaked.

Jerry drank, swallowed bravely and shakily passed the cup to Yonnie.

"What kind of hell's brew is that?" she gasped.

"My own special recipe. I mix it for my friends only," said Yonnie.

In due course, the cup came round again brimming with Yonnie's

224

"cock's tail." Encouraged by the sudden disappearance of my headache, I gulped it down. This time my whole interior seemed to take fire. I held onto my chair with both hands while the room reeled crazily round me. A strange numbness took hold of my hands and feet and started creeping up my arms and legs. In a daze, I watched Yonnie and Jerry recklessly slopping liquor into the cup and drinking it, at the same time beginning a wholesale and unrestrained relating of their life histories.

"I feel sick," I said. "I think I'm going to have a stroke."

Yonnie smiled sweetly.

"Haff another drink," he said. "Maybe you feel better."

"Maybe I will," I answered, groping for the bottle. "I certainly couldn't feel worse."

The third dose of Yonnie's special brew caused such dire results that I lost all further interest in life.

That was my first introduction to moonshine.

Inquiries made afterwards proved that all the drinks had originated in the backwoods stills which had been operating overtime in preparation for the party. Yonnie, anxious to outshine all the others and eager to impress the visiting firemen, had cooked up for us a cocktail containing samples of the various brews, well spiked with cheap rum and home-made blackberry wine. The result exceeded his wildest hopes.

Like a weird obbligato to the sound of the dancers' feet, Jerry's voice droned on in a series of anecdotes relative to her life in different places. Unheeding, Yonnie's high-pitched singsong tones ran counter to hers in a similar recital, and the whole blended with the uproar in the next room.

"—this man I met in New York . . . Reykjavik is so lofely in the sommer . . . How about a nice dreamy waltz? . . . Get out of there, you bog-trottin' mick! . . . Did you ever meet Izzy Gomez when you were in San Francisco, he had a dive down on the old Barbary Coast. . . . Little brown jug how I love thee-ee-ee . . . Vancouver . . . Iceland . . . Winnipeg . . . Bugger all Pete, kick this dog out! . . . LOO-EE!"

Blackie, flushed and dishevelled, came into the room once with a warning that we should leave at once if we were to catch the tide. I looked up at him hazily. Yonnie, with a gentle smile and a generous hand, poured out a cupful of liquid dynamite and offered it to him.

Blackie drank it off, shook himself like a dog, and reeled out with his hair all over his face. It was quite evident that time and tide no longer meant anything to him.

Jerry and Yonnie commenced another chapter of their life histories. Through the fog that clouded my brain I heard Yonnie sobbing in his soft broken English:

"I am so lonely—so lonely"—placing a hand on Jerry's shoulder—"I haff not efen a dog to keep me company."

"You can have Suey," wept Jerry, overcome by this pathetic picture.

Another bulky form appeared in the doorway and 'Lias lurched uncertainly in. "Oh, here you are. I've been looking all over for you. We've got to get crackin' if we want to get through the rapids before the tide turns."

Yonnie squeezed the last drops out of the bottle and handed the cup to him.

"Haff a drink," he said hospitably.

Two seconds later another redskin bit the dust.

The dance roared on unceasingly, the shrieks becoming more and more violent as the contents of the casks diminished.

"How about a nice dreamy waltz?" came in eldritch squeals from outside the door.

Jerry cringed and covered her ears with her hands.

"Don't let that ape in here—I've had all the dreamy waltzs I can stand."

"Reykjavik—Reykjavik!" moaned the homesick Yonnie, rocking himself to and fro.

The light in the doorway was blotted out as Joel strode in in a determined manner and, in a voice quite different from his usual shy, hesitant speech, informed us that the rest of us "slobs" could do as we liked, but that *he* was definitely going home.

226

Shakily I rose from my chair, holding onto its back with one hand while with the other I groped helplessly in the direction of the wall.

"I want my coat," I said, speaking with great care.

"What for?" said Jerry, looking up.

"Home!" I said making an ineffectual clutch at the wall and missing it.

"Who wants to go home?" inquired Jerry belligerently. "The party isn't nearly over yet—and stop clawing at that wall. Can't you see that your coat is on the other side of the room?"

I sat down again. Something told me that we were all behaving in a thoroughly disreputable fashion, but as nobody seemed capable of doing anything about it, the chair suddenly seemed a very safe place to be.

"Let's just stay here," I said hazily.

At this, I had a vague impression of being attacked by two tall, dark cyclones which had suddenly appeared from nowhere, pulled to my feet, leaned against a wall which appeared to be swinging violently from side to side, and shaken into my coat.

"Come on—stand up," said a voice.

I looked up into the laughing face of 'Lias. I looked at the arm which he was trying to push into my coat sleeve and realized that it was my own. I took a tentative step forward and the floor came up and hit me.

Once more I was pulled upright.

"Here's your fiddle," said Blackie, thrusting something into my arms.

Supported on either side by strong arms, I returned to the main room. Grave and polite, Big Pete and his Indian wife accepted our thanks for a lovely evening and wished us a safe journey home. I noticed that the guitar player, his head pillowed on his instrument, had fallen asleep on the bench. The banjo player, inaudible above the din, was pounding manfully on, stamping his heavy boots on the floor. I looked across at him and attempted to wave a good-bye, but Joel pulled me towards the door. As I stepped outside into the cold night air, the body of the dog, propelled from the toe of a large boot, shot past me. The last thing I heard above the Indian war-whoops and the white men's drunken yells was the Irishman's loudly expressed desire for a "nice dreamy walsh."

"Oh, how good that air feels!" I exclaimed as I weaved my way down to the boat, Joel and 'Lias steering me, and Big Pete walking in front carrying a lighted storm lantern.

Rain was falling, and the dinghy was half full of water when we reached it. Someone lifted me in bodily and I collapsed onto the seat, completely indifferent to the fact that my expensive dress was trailing in the sea. Once aboard the fishing boat, with the waves splashing beside us, I was revived somewhat by the fresh salt air. My head came back, likewise my headache.

The strong-and-silent men, silent no longer, were all talking at once, blaming each other for the fact that we were late for the tide and would have to shoot the rapids in the dark.

For once, I could not have cared less; in fact, the idea seemed tremendously amusing.

"I've always wanted to shoot rapids," I said recklessly.

We reached the entrance to the lagoon at seven in the morning. It was still dark as night and the cold rain was driving across the deck. Ahead of us flashed the white-crested rollers and the thunderous roar of the rapids drowned out the noise of the wind.

"Hold on, everybody—we're going in," shouted Joel.

I gripped the door-frame as the boat lurched sideways, then with a sickening crash we seemed to hit the floor of the ocean. I had barely time to notice the walls of black water towering up on either side of us before the boat was shot up to the top of the overfall, hung there suspended for a second or so, and then fell shuddering into the whirlpool on the other side.

We spun aimlessly round, hideously canted over to one side, the propeller racing in mid air, Joel and 'Lias struggling with the steering-wheel while Sonny and Blackie made ineffectual stabs with their boat-hooks over the sides in an effort to ward off half-submerged rocks. Incapable of any feeling but that of absolute panic, I clung to my door-frame. Then it was all over and we were shot out of the canyon as if we were something for which the sea had no further use.

This episode finished the sobering-up process for all of us. When we saw the prow of the boat cleaving the still dark waters of the lagoon, the brothers had reverted to their usual grim silence, and I was shaking with fright.

I was conscious only of a great feeling of relief as our escorts rowed us ashore and left us on the beach.

"Thanks, boys," said Jerry shakily. "We've had a wonderful time."

As we opened the door of the house, a cloud of dogs burst out in an ecstasy of welcome. I busied myself dishing out bowls of fish-head soup for them while Jerry staggered up the hill to see to the welfare of the goats and hens. The animals provided for, we fell fully dressed into bed.

It was three o'clock in the afternoon before we woke, sick, cold and miserable. I looked at my ruined shoes and salt-stained dress, and I looked at the dogs, who looked back with puzzled, sympathetic eyes.

"I feel awful. What happened?" I asked, turning to Jerry who was lighting the fire and making coffee.

"Don't ask me," she replied darkly. "I can't remember half of it. I feel as if we had had quite a night."

I felt my throat tenderly and coughed.

"My throat feels as if I had been gargling with carbolic acid."

"So does mine," retorted Jerry, "and I'll tell you one thing—if I had only known ten years ago that we were going out on a binge like that, I would never have paid to have my tonsils taken out."

Chapter 13

IT WAS several days before we saw our neighbours, and then late one afternoon 'Lias and Joel came in bringing the mail. Behind them, looking sheepish, and half buried in his outsized headgear, came Pat.

"I'd forgotten it was mail day," I said, wiping my dirty hands on my equally dirty blue jeans. "How's everybody? And how did the party go after we left?"

Everybody was recuperating nicely, they informed us laconically. The dance had run its appointed course, coming to an end only when the last man had passed out. Somebody had fallen out of a dinghy getting away from the shore, and Yonnie, in a gesture of heroism, had dived in to the rescue. As the water had been only two feet deep, he had struck headfirst in the mud and had had to be rescued himself.

"Seems as if we left too soon," I said regretfully. "That must have been worth seeing."

"Pity he didn't get pneumonia," said Jerry acidly, "but with all that liquor around I suppose it would be too much to hope for."

Pat looked at her reproachfully.

"Faith now, an' there wasn't a drink left in the barrel, and him shiverin' like a dog shittin' peach stones."

230

I caught Jerry's eye and suppressed a yelp of laughter.

"How about some coffee?" I said hastily.

The men sat down and I brought out the coffee-cups.

"I didn't see Vaino at the dance," said Jerry. "Doesn't he ever go to these affairs?"

"No!" said Joel explosively. "He doesn't dance or drink or smoke. All he does is talk and swill cocoa."

"There's worse things than cocoa," I said feelingly. "Next time I'll join him."

While Joel and 'Lias drank their usual three or four cups of coffee and smoked their cigarettes, Pat entertained us with a lively account of a recent visit to the island by the police boat.

"Them nosy spalpeens come snoopin' round here every so often," he said. "They don't mean no harm, but they have to do their job."

We found out that police visits were rare and completely futile. No sooner was the police boat seen in the vicinity then the news was promptly relayed from one fishing boat to another, and by the time the law had arrived at the island, all suspicious evidence such as home-made brew and out-of-season venison had been disposed of.

On this last occasion, Pat had not received the warning in time, and had been surprised with a fresh-killed deer in his store shed and a pot of venison stew on the stove; but Pat was not an Irishman for nothing. No sooner had he seen the two policemen coming across the beach than he had hauled the deer carcass out of the shed, pushed it into his bed and pulled the blankets over it. He then had invented a relative who was sick with stomach-ache. The venison stew had been explained away as beef that had gone a little "off."

"Sure, and I'd ask you to stay and have some," Pat had said with an innocent smile, "but I wouldn't want you to be havin' the stomach-ache the same as my cousin."

As 'Lias was leaving, he turned to me.

"I nearly forgot—I have a message for you."

"A message?" echoed Jerry.

"A friend of Angus's came out to meet the steamer this afternoon. He said the old man asked him to remind you that it's near Christmas. Dunno what he meant."

"We said we would take him a Christmas present," I explained. "It's not far off either. I do hope the weather is going to be fine; it's ages since we went to see him."

"You won't likely be seeing him for a while," said Joel, pulling up his coat collar. "It's going to snow."

His prophecy was correct. The snow began to fall that same night and continued steadily throughout the whole of the next day, by the end of which the aspect of the place had completely changed. We found ourselves in a white fairyland. When the snow ceased to fall, it began to freeze hard and for days we were unable to get away from the little cleared space that surrounded our house.

A strange icy stillness lay over everything. The trees, hung with heavy white snow-plumes, dropped their overburdened branches to the ground. The hillside was impassable. The lagoon froze over and we were completely marooned. All contact with our neighbours being broken, and being unable to move very far from the house, we found ourselves living in an atmosphere of timelessness which was intensified by the silence. As soon as the snow stopped falling, we scraped two paths, one to the water pipe and another to the wood-pile, after which we settled down to wait.

At night the northern lights rippled across the heavens like phosphorescent curtains, and each morning we woke to a leaden sky, a snow-spread landscape, and a sheet of dull grey ice where the sparkling blue waters of the lagoon used to be.

Setting our teeth, we would dive out of bed and into our heavy ski pants and sweaters, light the fires, and while breakfast was cooking, dash out of doors to the water pipe and brush our teeth and wash in the torrent of water and ice particles that was pouring out of it.

Breakfast was eaten with the table drawn as close to the stove as possible, and our feet, very often, in the oven.

When that was over, the animals had to be fed. Suey and the spaniels slept in boxes under the house at night, and were in splendid condition. Their coats were glossy and thick and their appetites enormous. Each morning when they heard us moving about over-head, they would scramble out of their beds and be eagerly waiting on the step when we came out of the house. They sat in a patient row, waiting for the pancakes and porridge left over from breakfast.

The hens were the next to appear on the scene. Breast-deep in snow, they struggled down from their house, now flying, now sinking in the drifts, and gathered round the back door. The empty porridge pot, put to soak under the water tap, was picked clean by a dozen eager beaks.

The young goats, their little noses purple with cold, huddled close to the house bleating pitifully. Used to wandering in the woods in search of food, they seemed stunned by the sudden onset of winter. There was nothing to eat in the white, wintry waste, and they looked at us so pleadingly that we found ourselves on occasion smuggling them into the warm comfort of the house, only to throw them out again in disgust when they misbehaved themselves, as they always did.

"I wouldn't mind them coming in," said Jerry, going round with a brush and shovel after one of these episodes, "if only we could rig them out in diapers."

After the breakfast dishes had been cleared away we attacked the woodpile. The logs were buried in snow and frozen together, and heavy blows with the axe were needed to separate them. Then the day's supply of wood had to be sawn up, split, and stacked in piles inside the hearth to thaw out. As the ice round the wood melted, little pools of water formed inside the fender and had to be constantly wiped up.

Buckets of water for household use had to be drawn from the water pipe. In fine weather, running outside to fill a pan with water each time we needed it had been no trouble; but with the intense cold, trips outside were cut to a minimum, and the water buckets were filled each morning with enough to last us for the day.

At first we used to leave the buckets on the porch just outside the door, but as each time we went to use the water we found it frozen solid, we began bringing them into the house and standing them in a row on the floor by the stove. This in turn produced its own problem when the dogs, deciding that the water in the buckets tasted better than that in their drinking-bowls, began dipping their noses in it.

"Can't you keep those slobbering spaniels out of our drinking-water?" complained Jerry.

"Oh, don't fuss. I read somewhere that a dog's mouth is as clean as a human's."

Jerry opened her mouth to say something, but thought better of it—which was probably just as well.

After the daily chores were done, the boats had to be attended to. Frozen fast in the ice, they had to be chopped free with an axe. We could hear the shouts of the brothers at the head of the lagoon as they drove their gas boat round and round in its ever narrowing circle of clear water. In the distance we saw Keijo rocking his boats backwards and forwards to keep them free of the encroaching ice. Following the example set by our neighbours, we ran out to join them in a losing battle with the elements. Eventually, of course, the boats would be frozen in for the winter; but the present cold spell might turn out to be a short one, and it would be foolish to expose them unnecessarily to the danger of ice damage.

The usual procedure after breaking the thin ice at the water's edge was to slip on the slime-covered stones and fall in. Then, without bothering to change, we each climbed into a boat and with soaking garments and frozen feet, we stood and rocked them violently from one side to the other. The ice cracked and broke with a wrenching, splintering sound and churned about us, great wedges rearing their sharp sides up in the air and sliding silently under the black water.

As each morning brought the same performance to be gone through again, the first rather amusing novelty of it quickly wore off. Each day the ice grew thicker and harder, until one could have driven a dog team down the centre of the lagoon with ease.

Then came the day when the ice was too heavy to break. We

heard no more distant shouts from the brothers, and Keijo retired behind a wall of silence and snow for the rest of the freeze-up.

The trail to the lake was covered with snowdrifts and impassable, consequently the water pipe had to be kept from freezing at all costs. We kept the tap open and allowed the water to run day and night, but frequently ice would form in the pipe and it had to be watched constantly. The water came in spurts and explosions and brought showers of ice splinters with it. Often at night we would wake and listen for the coughing, bubbling noise that told us that all was well with the water supply. Sometimes we would wake to a horrible silence, and that meant a dash out of a warm bed into an arctic temperature to see to the pipe.

So used did we get to waking at frequent intervals during the night that the pipe never had a chance to freeze solid, and a sharp jerk often would dislodge any ice blocking the passage, and restore the flow of water. We would go back to bed, praying for morning and a slightly warmer temperature.

In spite of our extra winter provisions, we now found our food supply running down. The steamer, ploughing through the stormy seas outside, no longer stopped to deliver mail and supplies. The last of the vegetables in the garden had gone. Fishing was out of the question.

Once or twice, driven by an urge for fresh meat, Jerry had taken the gun and gone off into the fairylike whiteness of the forest in a vain search for game.

"I feel like Hiawatha during the famine season," she said as she stumbled away in the snow. The hunting trips failed to provide anything for our diminishing larder. The forest was silent and deserted. Not a bird rustled in the branches and even the squirrels had disappeared. The only sign of life we ever saw was an occasional gull, walking carefully over the ice.

In spite of the cold and the solitude, we were not unhappy. We sat by the fire and read, we worked up our circulation by splitting wood, we ran up and down the narrow strip of beach in front of the house tossing snowballs for the dogs. Still possessing the better part of a hundred-pound sack of sugar, we made pans full of toffee and fudge and froze it in the snow.

About four o'clock in the afternoon, the dull grey twilight which was our day changed to the cold blackness of night. Mountains of wood were piled by the hearth so that we would not have to go outside unnecessarily and the lamps were filled with our fast-diminishing supply of oil. Then followed the long winter evenings in the log house, with all the fires roaring and the coffee-pot bubbling on the stove.

Through the big windows we looked at the moon hanging between the stems of the firs and flooding the frozen bay with cold light; and, sitting one on either side of the hearth, with the dogs sleeping at our feet, we smiled across at each other contentedly.

Before we went to bed the dogs had to be put into their boxes under the house. One by one they would be tucked in, the blankets pushed round each sleek body, while their eager tongues licked our faces as we bent over them.

This done, we would stand awhile on the shore, looking at the dark motionless firs, the long purple shadows and the icy-cold sky above, and listen to the occasional crack of a branch in the forest, breaking under its weight of snow.

We seemed to be living on a dead planet.

Giving a last look at the sputtering water pipe, we would go back to the house where the big square galvanized bathtub was standing on the stove, full of hot water ready for our baths. Then a final piling on of wood and into bed we would go.

When the fires had flickered out, and the cold crept through the house, we snuggled deeper under the blankets and listened to the ice cracking outside like pistol shots as the tide quietly rose and fell beneath it.

In the morning there would be the same eerie stillness and the grey snow-light filtering through the windows, and our breath hanging in clouds on the chilly air.

"Your turn to get up and light the fire."

"'Tis not! I lit it yesterday."

236

"Cripes, if it wasn't for the animals, I'd never get up. I'd stay here and hibernate till spring."

Finding ourselves confined to the house a great deal, we took out the radio again and listened to the outside world, feebly carried to us by the dying batteries. We found it strangely uninteresting, and as we listened to the strident blares of a dance band, the false enthusiasm of radio commercials, and below it all, in an ominous rumble, the reports of international strife and industrial unrest, we looked round our still, white, frozen world and were more than ever—content.

Just before Christmas, a thaw set in and we saw with glee the ice melt on the lagoon. Torrents of rain fell and washed away the snow and we slept peacefully at night without waking to listen to the water pipe.

We had another cause for rejoicing when we were able to get our Christmas mail and much-needed supplies. Joel and 'Lias took their boat out and brought back several boxes full of gifts in addition to our regular food supplies.

All our friends had remembered us and with unusual forethought had packed up boxes of food such as they knew we would not be likely to buy. There were a dressed turkey, fruit of all descriptions, nuts, sausages, pickles, shortbread, twelve iced Christmas cakes, dozens of boxes of candy, cigarettes, mince pies, a bottle of rum, books and magazines. Three boxes from California contained all the trimmings necessary for a Christmas tree, and some avocados. There were bath salts, and warm woollen underwear; there were even presents for the dogs.

Sundi came over and watched the unpacking of the boxes with eyes round with wonder. Keijo never observed the Christmas festival —it was "great foolishness" in his opinion; but his wife, after sampling a little of all the good things we had received, went back to her own bare home and the company of the dour and silent Keijo, looking a little discontented.

Keijo's philosophy of life lived "the hard way" did not make for gracious living, and during her occasional visits to us, her eyes would rest on our comfortable chairs and thick rugs with longing.

"Why don't you make Keijo buy you some chairs and things?" I asked.

Her eyes grew big with horror at the mere thought.

"*He* not liking anyt'ing like that," she replied.

"Then why don't you leave him and come and live with us?" demanded Jerry bluntly.

A burst of delighted and half-fearful giggles followed this remark.

Our relations with Keijo had become rather strained of late and we began to suspect that after her visits to us, his wife had returned home with a heart full of courage and a head full of new ideas. The frequent disputes resulting from this state of affairs brought down Keijo's wrath on our heads.

"The hard way is the best—I always living the hard way," he said, storming into our house after his wife had told him about the Christmas parcels.

"Why live the hard way?" we argued. "Life is meant to be enjoyed, not endured."

"You can't living without a lot of humbug," said he, bringing out the latest addition to his English vocabulary. "You can't eating without a lot of humbug—your house full of humbug," waving a contemptuous hand towards the furniture.

"Humbug, my eye," said Jerry sarcastically. "I suppose you would like to see us eating dry bread for breakfast and sitting on orange boxes?"

Keijo strode off, his ice-blue eyes fairly glowing with rage and loudly congratulating himself that he was not "born on a chester-field."

We put Keijo's lecture out of our minds and went off in a hilarious mood to look for a Christmas tree small enough to bring into the house without our first having to take the roof off. Once found, the tree was cut, trimmed and decorated and all our presents arranged beneath it.

The dogs ploughed excitedly among the piles of wrapping paper, hoping to find something we had overlooked. Little parcels of candy and dried fruits were wrapped for our different friends, and a grass basket filled with oranges and shiny red apples set aside for Angus.

"We'll take it to him Christmas day," I said. "The sea is calm now, and we promised."

On Christmas Eve Joel and his three brothers came to see us. They paused in the doorway, looking at the tree and the piles of presents with amazement.

"Sure looks pretty," said Sonny, coming closer to the tree and touching the coloured glass balls, "a star on top and everything."

He stood looking at it in admiration until his elder brother touched him on the shoulder.

"Show the girls the present you have got for them."

His face lighted up as he put his hand deep into his coat pocket and drew out a small grey kitten. The little creature, lost in his huge fist, opened a tiny pink mouth and gave a frightened mew.

Jerry and I both reached for it with delighted squeals.

"Oh, the darling! How did you know we wanted a kitten?"

"The old cat had kittens a few weeks ago—we kept this one as a surprise for you."

Jerry poured out a saucer of milk for the kitten and warded off the inquisitive nuzzling of the dogs, while the boys continued their grave inspection of the tree ornaments and the strings of Christmas cards.

Later, seated by the fire, we displayed our presents to them. They wrinkled their noses disdainfully over the bath salts, made appreciative inroads on the candy and cigarettes, studied the avocados with suspicion, and were completely overwhelmed when, as they left, we presented them with a large box filled with samples of everything that we had had sent to us.

"Shucks, there was no need for you to do that," they said, scarlet and abashed. "Looks like you won't have any left for yourselves."

The remainder of Christmas Eve was spent playing with the kitten. On account of a dispute between us concerning its sex, we decided to name it Sarah John, reasoning that if future events warranted, we could easily drop the John.

Before going to bed, we went through our usual routine of putting the dogs into their boxes under the house and presented each one with his Christmas present—a rubber bone to chew on. Then we walked up the hill with our lantern to say good-night to the chickens and goats.

The chickens murmured uneasily as we shone the lantern on them, and the goats, hearing our voices, bleated softly in welcome as they lay on their beds of dried bracken.

"Happy Christmas!" said Jerry, stooping to stroke them.

Outside the sky had cleared and the stars burned brightly down on the motionless trees. There were no decorated stores or brightly lit streets and none of the trappings of a modern Christmas, but the "Silent night, holy night" feeling was pronounced.

"Get out your violin and we'll play some carols before we go to bed," I said after we had reached the house, "—and leave the doors open so that the animals can hear us."

On Christmas morning, after a leisurely breakfast, we were performing our daily tasks of feeding the livestock, cutting the firewood and tidying up the house, when we were startled to see Vaino's power boat roar into the bay. Tossing the anchor over the side, he waded ashore in his rubber hip-boots and walked across the beach to the house.

He pushed open the door with the easy familiarity peculiar to the islanders and announced that he had come to take us back with him to join his Christmas party.

We hesitated, thinking of our Christmas turkey and the piles of food on the kitchen shelves.

"It'll keep," said Vaino briefly.

"We can't go," I said. "We promised to see Angus today and we have a present for him."

"He'll be there tomorrow," said Vaino.

"It may be rough tomorrow, and besides we have a kitten now and we can't leave it alone."

"Bring it along then," said Vaino patiently.

To all our arguments he presented an implacable stubbornness;

and at last, worn down with battering against this wall of iron determination, we gave in. Leaving food for the goats and chickens, we lifted the dogs into the boat, rolled Sarah John up in a woollen scarf and allowed ourselves to be carried off to his house.

"I still think we should have gone to see Angus," I said in sulky tones as we left the lagoon behind.

Vaino made no reply to this and presently we turned into his horseshoe-shaped harbour.

A number of boats were anchored there and we saw that we were not the only guests invited to eat Christmas dinner with Vaino. The guilty feeling caused by the breaking of my promise to call on Angus died away on our walk through the forest; and when we entered Vaino's house we found a large and festive gathering there. The newspapered walls were covered with garlands of cedar, the cavernous fireplace was a blazing mass of crackling logs, and an air of jollity and good fellowship prevailed.

The season's greetings were called out in several different languages as we entered, and we were drawn into the middle of a happy crowd standing in front of the fire.

Vaino disappeared into the kitchen, from which feminine chatter, appetizing smells and the clatter of dishes were issuing. We watched with amazement while three women, under his supervision, spread the long refectory table. One of them we recognized as "Loo-ee," the Dutchman's woman; Vaino took each of the other two by the hand and with a gracious gesture, presented them to us as being wives of two of the fishermen present. We shook hands gravely.

One of the women was a Dane, flat-footed and sallow, with stringy tan-coloured hair. With downcast eyes she muttered something inaudible and fled back to the kitchen. The other, a tiny creature with tragic dark eyes set in a Madonna-like face, looked at us with a world of sorrow in her unhappy countenance and whispered a greeting in strongly accented English before returning to her duties.

I looked after them thoughtfully. With the exception of Keijo's wife Sundi, Jerry and I had never been able to make friends with the few white women on the island. We found that the hard way of life for women seemed to act as an efficient antidote to any intellectual development, and against the more forceful characters of the men, their colourless personalities faded into the background like pale shadows.

I tried to express my views to Vaino.

"I suppose it is because they have not had much education," I finished with unconscious snobbery.

Vaino looked quickly at me. "That depends on what you mean by education. If you mean mere book learning—no, they have never had that advantage; but they have had an education in hard work and suffering such as you have never known. That last girl you looked at so scornfully is a D.P. and her first husband and child died most uncomfortably in a concentration camp."

I felt my face flushing.

"I really didn't mean that the way it sounded," I said. "I mean that they don't seem to want to be friends with us."

"Have you *really* tried to be friends with them?" asked Vaino in tones of irony.

Thinking back, I had to admit that I had not tried very hard.

Vaino turned away in the direction of the kitchen again and I scowled into the glass eyes of a stuffed squirrel which was clinging to a dusty branch on the mantel shelf.

"I wish we hadn't come. I wish we had gone to see Angus instead," I whispered to Jerry.

Further wishful thinking was interrupted a few minutes later by a shout of laughter which greeted a procession which was coming out of the kitchen bearing smoking platters of food. Vaino, in the lead, was wearing a chef's white cap and apron and brandishing a carving knife and fork. Behind him came the three women and several of the men carrying dishes of food, attractively garnished.

Summoned to the feast, we stared in admiration at the table which was sagging under the load of food. Everything with the exception of the coffee, the sugar, the spices, and the flour used in the baking of bread and cake had been produced on the place. At the head of the table a gargantuan roast of venison rested on a bed of glazed potatoes and parsnips. Serving dishes all round the sides were laden with baked red snapper, dripping with butter; jellied chicken, smoked salmon, and every kind of vegetable. There were winter cabbage, sprouts and kale fresh from the garden; canned peas, asparagus, corn and tiny spiced carrots which had been put down during the summer months.

There were rows of pies and bottled fruits, cakes, Danish pastry filled with preserves made from wild berries, fresh crusty loaves, pounds of yellow butter, pitchers of fresh milk, and cream so thick that it refused to pour. There were also fresh oysters and crabs, dishes of dried plums and crystallized wild honey, and small glasses of home-made wine.

Jerry and I looked at the spread with open mouths, and then with Vaino's quizzical gaze fixed on us, Jerry said:

"You know, there's many a millionaire that doesn't live as well as this."

"Remember that," said Vaino, "you two who are always thinking about money. Look at me—I have fuel enough for a hundred years. I have food enough to feed an army and all it costs me is the labour of producing it. I have beauty everywhere; and above all, I have freedom and peace of mind. What use is money?"

"You still have to buy coal oil, boat gas and clothes," said Jerry, unconvinced and determined to have the last word. "There are some things that you can't produce."

"Well, if it comes to that, I could make clothes out of skins; the early settlers made their own candles; and boat gas is a luxury one can do without—after all, there is nothing nicer than a sail-boat."

These remarks touched off a discussion on how little a person actually needed to live on. During the meal, notes were compared by the guests on their living expenses, and Jerry and I received a lesson on domestic economy that effectively silenced us. We were told of hard times when the woods had been searched for edible fungi, dandelion roots roasted and ground for coffee, the tops of young bracken shoots cooked as a vegetable, and seaweed used in a variety of ways.

"What about sugar and flour?" I ventured. "Can a person find a substitute for those?"

"If you have potatoes, you don't need flour," said Vaino, "and sugar is not a necessity. You are better off without it."

"We had a dream once," said Jerry wistfully, "that we might be able to live without money, but somehow it hasn't worked out."

"It can be done. It *has* been done. Supposing that the world economy collapsed overnight—the hardy souls would manage to live even without money."

"And the others?" I asked.

Vaino's grey eyes looked hard. "You know what happened to the lotos eaters."

The food melted away under the hungry onslaughts of the islanders, and Vaino, boasting of his exploits, drew answering stories and anecdotes from the others.

We listened to tales of rapids besides which the turbulent entrance to Quiet Waters paled into insignificance. Stories of shipwreck were frequent and violent death treated with a light-hearted indifference.

One man had seen his partner killed by wolves. Another had lost a lifelong friend when he was swallowed up in a crevasse as they were crossing an ice-field.

"Couldn't you get him out?" I asked, horrified.

"He was hurt real bad," said the man simply. "We couldn't get down to him. We just stayed there till he died, and then went on."

The Dutchman broke into what he evidently considered a wildly hilarious story of an occasion when he had been offered twenty-five dollars to bring a sick trapper out of the wilds on his boat. The trapper had died shortly after the trip commenced, and the Dutchman, intent on collecting his twenty-five dollars, had dragged the body across the deck and lashed the feet to the rail to keep it from being washed overboard.

"She wass blowing a gale," he chuckled reminiscently. "Eferry

244

time I look ofer my shoulder, dere vas old Tom swinging backwards and forwards across de deck."

Nobody showed any inclination to hurry over the meal, and the dishwashing and sorting out of plates and cutlery loaned by the different guests went on through the afternoon. The men sat round the hearth, smoking and talking.

Darkness came early and a storm sprang up that shook the house. The wind screamed and moaned in the chimney and rattled the windows. Vaino hurried out to lock up his livestock and the fishermen pulled on their oilskin coats and went down to the beach to see to their boat anchors, returning in a little while drenched with spray.

"Sure is blowing out there," said one. "Guess we won't be going home in this."

While the women prepared more coffee and sandwiches, Vaino refilled the glasses, and the men raised them to each other with shouts of "Skoal" and "Prosit"; then they drew closer to the fire, and their talk turned again to tales of storms and shipwreck. They told of queer superstitions, and old European legends of ghost lights, and of sea witches who bind up the wind in knots of rope—until, with each fresh gust, I imagined evil faces peering through the windows, and the rattling of the casements seemed to be caused by clawlike hands tapping on the glass. With a shiver, I recalled Sundi's words: "It having what you call spooks."

Midnight came and the storm showed no sign of abating. The fishermen prepared to spend the night on their boats, planning to leave for home as soon as the wind subsided. Jerry and I were to sleep in the loft.

We accompanied the guests down to the shore to see them board their boats, moving slowly through the lashing trees in Indian file swinging hurricane lanterns. As we neared the shore, the roar of the sea became deafening and we could hardly make our way against the wind. The dinghys pulled up in a row on the beach were quickly pushed out into deep water, and oars splashed in the sullen waves as they were rowed towards their parent boats anchored further out.

Now and then a watery moon showed through the wind-torn clouds, and by its pale light we could see the glistening black rollers thundering up the beach like an army of marching giants, and the white surf breaking on the rock at the entrance to the bay.

We watched till the dinghies had disappeared into the shadow of the bigger boats, and for a while stood and looked at the riding-lights as they rocked up and down in the comparative shelter of the bay. Then we turned, whistled to the dogs, and went back to the house.

As we closed the door behind us, the clamour of the wind in the treetops died away to a dull murmur. The room looked warm and cosy in the lamplight. Vaino was sitting in front of the fire staring thoughtfully into the glowing embers while he stirred a cup of cocoa.

He looked up as we entered, and pointing to the jug standing in the hearth said, "Help yourself. You must be cold."

I poured myself a cup of the thick, sickly liquid and wandered idly about the room studying the newspaper-covered walls.

I came to a stop before a highly technical article on international finance.

"I thought you weren't interested in money?" I said.

Vaino glanced over his shoulder at me, and pouring out another cup of cocoa sipped it in silence for a while.

"I'm not," he said at last, "but I am interested in what other people think about it."

"I wish I were a millionaire," I said longingly. "It's not that I want money for myself, but I could help so many people. I would buy the boys a new engine for their boat, and fix up Angus's house—you can see daylight through the roof—and I would give Christian enough money so that he wouldn't have to trap any more animals."

Vaino laughed scornfully.

"If you were a millionaire you probably wouldn't do any of those things, and if you did, you wouldn't be helping any of those people. The boys are quite capable of earning money to buy themselves an engine and they will appreciate it all the more if they have to work for it. Angus wouldn't like you to fix up his house—he is much too proud to accept favours from anyone; and Christian would only spend the money on drink. When he is out in the woods trapping, he stays healthy and sober. Money would be the ruin of him."

He set his cup down in the hearth.

"A person gets the fate he deserves. It is no use trying to change it for him."

I looked at him suspiciously. "Did you think that one up by yourself or is it somebody else's idea?"

"No," smiled Vaino, "it's an idea that quite a few people have discovered for themselves."

"Just another one of your great truths," I said, coming back to the hearth and picking up the kitten which was playing with Suey's tail. "Do you think that some day *I* will discover a great truth?"

Vaino smiled as he took down a candlestick from the shelf above the hearth.

"I think you both are already discovering one." He lighted the candle and handed it to us.

"You will find extra blankets on the cots in the loft. Good-night, I hope you sleep well."

Up in the loft, we looked about us. The candlelight flickered on the cots and the old wooden chest which were the only furnishings. The house creaked in the storm and the branches of trees whipped across the tiny window.

I sat down on one of the cots and kicked off my shoes.

Jerry, sitting on the edge of the second cot, was tucking Sarah John under the covers.

"This mattress feels awfully lumpy—I bet it's stuffed with corn husks."

I looked at her unseeingly. "I keep thinking about Angus. He will have been waiting for us and wondering why we didn't come."

"There will be lots of time between Christmas and New Year," said Jerry, crawling carefully into bed. "He won't mind as long as we go some time during the holiday season."

We blew out the candle, stretched out underneath the blankets and lay listening to the shrieks of the wind and the rattling windows.

Warm air rose from the big room below and presently we fell asleep.

Next morning, the storm had died down, and as we woke, we saw the window which the previous night had been glistening with raindrops now framing a square of blue sky. Outside we could hear the faint barking of the dogs.

Dressing hurriedly, we ran down to the main room. There were breakfast dishes on the table and a coffee-pot and a pan full of porridge were keeping hot on the hearth. Through the open window we could see Vaino standing in his "chapel" surrounded by a carpet of venison bones and a quartet of adoring dogs.

"I suppose he's talking to Old Whiskers," I said. "I wonder what he says?"

"Whatever it is, I bet it isn't anything original," said Jerry in scathing tones.

While I was pouring coffee, Vaino appeared in the doorway.

"Pour some for me. I had breakfast on one of the boats with the boys before they left, but that was early on."

"We must go too," I said. "There are the goats and the chickens to feed."

"There is no need to hurry, it's still pretty rough outside."

In spite of the high seas and the scudding clouds, we were eager to return to Quiet Waters, and staying just long enough to wash up the breakfast dishes, we picked up our coats, called the dogs and insisted that we must go.

As the power boat heaved up and down through the waves, I thought guiltily of our broken promise to Angus.

"Tomorrow," I thought, "tomorrow we will go and see him whatever happens."

Chapter 14

THE NEXT day was cold and windy and when we rowed down to the rapids and saw the turbulent waves outside, we realized that there was no possibility of our going to see Angus.

"I knew we should have gone on Christmas Day," I said fretfully.

"Well, it's no use worrying about it—Angus will understand and the bad weather won't last forever," replied Jerry.

The bad weather did last, and for the next few days while waiting for a break in the storm, we consoled ourselves by gorging on unaccustomed luxuries, smoking imported cigarettes, and splashing lavender bath salts into the old tin tub with a lavish hand.

"Vaino can say what he likes about material things," said Jerry, immersing the lower half of herself in highly perfumed bath water, "but it's much pleasanter to coddle your body than to feed your mind."

The end of December came. Joel and his brothers had invited us to welcome in the New Year with them.

New Year's Eve saw us dressed for the party in our oilskins and groping our way down to the water's edge in blinding rain, baling out the boat by the light of a storm lantern and unscrambling the wet, slimy ropes. Then, each taking an oar, we set off on our long row up the lagoon in the dark.

On our way, we stopped in to wish Keijo and Sundi the compliments of the season. We found them in their immaculate but uncomfortable kitchen. Keijo was sitting on a straight-backed kitchen chair thumbing through the mail-order catalogue; Sundi was perched on the wood-box, staring at the lamp. She beamed cordially at us, but Keijo was grimmer than usual. Our friendship with Vaino was a constant source of annoyance to him.

"He bad friend for you—I telling you for your own good," he said on hearing where we had spent Christmas Day.

"He's just jealous," said Jerry as we rowed away. "Up to now we have always run to him for advice; he can't bear to think that we prefer Vaino."

Pulling hard over the black water and guided by a faint glimmer of light coming from the windows of Joel's house, we bumped finally into the float, crawled across its coating of green slime and, soaked with rain and spray, made our way up to the house.

The door opened and a rush of warm air and light came out to meet us. Our hosts, if inarticulate, were full of hospitality. They piled wood on the heater, took our dripping oilskins, exclaimed over Jerry's wet feet, and ended up by bringing her some colossal grey wool socks and a pair of rush slippers that only needed a sail added to transform them into two good-sized Chinese junks.

As a contribution to the evening's entertainment, we had brought with us one of our remaining Christmas cakes, some mince pies, candy, and cigarettes. The brothers had made some exceedingly hefty-looking sandwiches and brewed a gallon pot of coffee.

The party was on.

We danced to the gramophone, all very informally. Sometimes the men danced with us, sometimes they danced solemnly with each other.

When that novelty wore off, we played cards. Joel and his brothers knew nothing of the intricacies of bridge, so we played Hearts and Old Maid.

There were no cocktails. We drank to the New Year in coffee and at midnight we all trooped out onto the verandah and saluted its arrival with a round fired from a double-barrelled shotgun, accompanied by the remark that we hoped it knocked Keijo out of bed.

Soon after this, we collected our oilskins, said good-bye to our hosts and started off down the dark lagoon again, speculating cheerfully as to what our friends in the city were doing.

"I don't envy them one bit," I said virtuously, peering ahead for the shore-line. "They are probably getting a terrific bun on and looking kind of red-eyed and bedraggled by now."

"Look where you're going," warned Jerry, "—you have passed the end of our street. Pull on your left and never mind about who looks how."

Paddling carefully, we drifted in to shore, stepped over the side of the boat into the cold sea-water, dragged the boat up above high-water mark, and went into the house and the boisterous welcome of the dogs.

And so the festive season passed.

Next morning we woke early and sailed into a breakfast of hot-cakes and maple syrup with gusto.

"This is the first time in my life that I woke after a New Year's Eve party without my head feeling like a beehive and a taste in my mouth as if a Chinese family had moved out," said Jerry, helping herself to more hotcakes.

"Last year," I said, unhappily recalling late discomforts, "I seem to remember breakfasting on stomach powders."

That night after we had put the dogs to bed, we stood on the beach looking at the dark water and the sky.

"The rain has stopped. The stars are shining," said Jerry, tilting her head back. "Just listen. Did you ever hear such silence?"

"The storm is over," I answered, "—I can hear the rapids. That means the wind is from the west. Tomorrow will be fine, and we can go and see Angus."

But during the night came the second freeze-up and a heavy fall of snow, and once again we found ourselves cut off from all communication with our neighbours.

This time we found the business of chopping the boats free of ice and getting up at night to attend to the water pipe a distinct hardship. We wearied with gazing at the snow-bound landscape. The stoves gaped like ravenous monsters and the sixteen wet doggy feet pattering in and out kept us constantly mopping up the floors.

Once again our supplies began to run low. We had no fruit or vegetables, the butter gave out, and instead of tea and coffee, we were reduced to drinking water. Worst of all we had used up all the cigarette tobacco.

"No baccy, no papers," said Jerry, turning over the empty tins in a vain search for enough dust to make one cigarette.

After a thorough rummaging through all the cupboards, we came up with an experimental mixture of old tea-leaves, thyme and sage, rolled up in a piece of toilet paper and gummed with molasses.

The result was disastrous but it effected a saving on our sinking food supply, because we were both so completely nauseated that it was at least two days before we could bring ourselves to open another can of beans.

Sometimes we struggled over the rocks at low tide to the entrance of the lagoon in order to catch a glimpse of the pale wintry sun shining outside on the sea, but its rays never penetrated the icy fastness of our inlet.

Along with our yearning for sunlight was a perpetual craving for fresh greens, salads, and citrus fruits. We sickened over our starchy diet and vowed that once the winter was over, we would never again touch another bean or grain of rice.

The wicked cold continued through January and then the first sign of life appeared in the form of sea lettuce, which began to grow in thin transparent sheets on the rocks below the water's edge. Remembering the straits to which our island friends had been reduced at different times, we gathered it, boiled and ate it and found that it seemed to satisfy a system starved for vitamins.

A little later the ice began to melt, and the hens scratched contentedly in the soft earth beneath the trees. Chilblained hands began to heal and we put aside our heavy rubber boots.

With the first real thaw, the sound of Vaino's boat was heard roaring up the lagoon, and he came in laden with all the things for which we had been so famished—apples from his storehouse, winter cabbage, peppergrass which he had grown in pots indoors, and a large piece of beef from a recently butchered cow. There were even bones for the dogs, who dragged them off into the shelter of the trees and chewed steadily for hours.

"Eat plenty of meat now to make up for the vitamins you have been missing, and eat the cabbage raw. It's better for you," said Vaino on hearing of our food shortages. "When you live in places like these, you should make provision for the bad times."

We told him about the meals of sea lettuce and he nodded approvingly.

"Good, you are learning. All the minerals the body needs are in the sea. You should eat the seaweed and you could have dug up moss and eaten that too, and the tips of the juniper bushes. All the men know enough to eat juniper after long periods of starchy diet."

Joel and his brothers came to see how we had fared during our period of isolation and brought us smoked salmon from their own stores.

Of Keijo we saw nothing. According to Sundi, who paid us a hurried and surreptitious visit, the sight of Vaino coming into the lagoon laden with gifts of food had been sufficient to throw him into a frenzy of rage, and the further presents of fish from Joel had roused his ire to such an extent that he had summarily ordered his wife to stay away from us altogether.

"*He* say you should not living on other people," she told us in subdued tones, "but I am thinking that people should helping each other."

We missed her cheerful round face, harmless gossip, and awe-filled, excited giggles as she listened to our strongly expressed views on woman's rights.

When the last of the ice had drifted out of the lagoon, we set out for our long-deferred visit to Angus. We took the basket of fruit, which, in spite of our starvation diet, we had managed to keep intact. After a careful examination of the boats for possible damage done by the ice, we rowed out of the inlet into the open for the first time since Christmas Day. We rowed slowly, looking at the misty sky, the islands floating on the quiet sea, and the trail of smoke on the horizon which showed the passing of a ship.

We drew in long breaths of the fresh cold air and chattered gaily as we rowed along, picturing Angus's surprised pleasure at seeing us and his bashful acceptance of the delayed present.

As we came within sight of Angus's house, Jerry stopped rowing.

"There's another boat tied up to the wharf. He must have visitors."

She rested on her oars and looked uneasily about.

"There's no smoke coming out of the chimney. I don't think he's there."

"Don't be silly. There's his boat, of course he's there."

We tied up to the float and climbed aboard Angus's boat.

"He's probably in the cabin," I said confidently and called his name: "Angus! Angus, we're here!"

There was no answering hail. The pilot-house door was pad-locked and a strange lifelessness hung over everything.

"Angus!" I shouted in sudden fear, "Angus!"

A faint sound came from the other boat, and turning quickly, I saw the pilot-house door open and a stocky, bearded figure emerge from the opening.

"Where's Angus?" I asked.

The man looked at us in silence for a minute; then, with an accent as strong as that of Angus, he replied bluntly: "Angus is dead and in his grave."

"No—oh no!" I said unbelieving.

"I'm thinkin' ye'll be the friends he was expectin'."

Too stunned to answer, I stared miserably at him and it was Jerry who broke the silence.

"When did he die?"

"The day after Christmas," answered the fisherman. "Come in an' I'll tell ye."

We followed him into the little cabin. Even in my misery I

noticed the neatness and cleanliness of the old man's living-quarters. The air was warm from the tiny oil stove, beside which a comfortable chair was drawn up. Across the boxed-in engine a big tabby cat lay sleeping and an open Bible and a pair of spectacles lay on the table.

"Sit ye doon," said the man hospitably, pointing to the bunk.

Still dazed by the news, we sat down and listened while he told us his story.

An old acquaintance of Angus's, he had called to see him just before Christmas and had been persuaded to stay over and meet what Angus called his "lady friends."

"Aye, he thocht a lot o' ye twa; he was rare disappointed when ye didna come."

I thought of Vaino's Christmas party with a sick heart.

"He kept waitin' for ye," went on the old fisherman reproachfully. "He said ye promised."

We said nothing—there was nothing to say; and after waiting for a minute or two, the fisherman continued with the tale.

The day after Christmas, Angus had been found lying on the floor of his cabin—dead. His son had been notified and had come up from the city to take charge of the funeral arrangements, and Angus's tired old body had been taken to town for burial.

"They should ha' buried him here," said the fisherman with a shake of his head. "What would Angus want wi' a gran' funeral and a cemetery?"

The English bitch had come also and had ordered the burning of all Angus's treasures, which she stigmatized as "old rubbish," and had locked up the house and put it up for sale.

"I thocht ye might come some time and wonder wha' happened," said the fisherman. "For Angus's sake I bided here to tell ye." He paused and looked at us a little sadly. "I can be leavin' noo."

I stood up and stared unseeingly at the cellophane-wrapped basket of fruit with its gay bow of red ribbon.

"We brought this for Angus," I said. "Perhaps you would like to have it."

255

The old man's face lighted up as he looked at the gift and he smiled gratefully.

"Angus said ye were aye guid to him."

I placed the fruit beside the open Bible on the table. "He was the one that was good—not us."

I turned to the doorway. "We'll just walk up to the house before we go, and take a last look."

We found the house as the fisherman had said, securely padlocked and wearing that forlorn, neglected look common to empty houses.

The deer no longer lay on the verandah and in the garden was a large blackened circle containing the ashes of a fire. The lilac bushes were seared with the heat from the flames, and as we looked we saw among the fragments of charred wood and clothing, the remains of the gramophone and a few broken records.

We walked back to the wharf in silence. Ahead of us we saw the boat belonging to the bearded fisherman sailing seawards.

A sudden sense of desolation swept over me. "Let's go quickly," I said.

We rowed away without looking back.

Our grief over the death of Angus brought forth a few perfunctory condolences from the Nelsons, but the best they could offer in the way of consolation was the fact that Angus was an old man and his time had come.

Vaino was not even consolatory.

"Life is such a transient thing, you can't afford to waste any of it being miserable."

"I know," I replied in utter dejection, "but I can't help remembering that we promised to go and see him and then broke our promise."

"So it's not the loss of Angus that is bothering you. It is merely a guilt complex, and like a good Christian you are wallowing in a sort of moral self-flagellation."

I turned away, recognizing the usual grain of truth in Vaino's remarks, and for the next few days I made a determined effort to face facts. Angus was gone and no amount of grieving would bring him back. For the rest of us, life had to go on.

February had given place to March, and the first rays of sun penetrated the dark lagoon. Our depression lifted when we looked out the first morning and saw a shaft of golden light striking down between the trees.

We ran outside and let it shine down on us in all its glowing warmth, and the tension and weariness caused by the long cold winter coupled with the death of Angus gradually left us. The dogs joined us and blinked their gentle brown eyes as they gazed upwards, and the hens crowded together on a patch of sunny ground and preened their feathers with contented murmurings. Describing it to Vaino afterwards, Jerry said it was "like a prayer meeting only more cheerful."

After this, the weather grew warmer and more springlike. The croaking of bullfrogs sounded from the swamps. Birds and squirrels appeared once more in the trees and the woods rustled with life. The wild April nights were filled with evasive perfumes and in the scented darkness the distant and soul-stirring calls of the returning geese dropped from the sky.

"It's spring at last," we said, sniffing the heady air. "It's time to live again."

"It looks as though our bank balance was getting pretty low."

This ominous discovery was made one glorious spring day when we were rowing home with the mail. It was our practice to open all the mail on the way home and while one of us did the rowing, the other read the contents aloud.

The words sent a little chill through me.

During our year on the island we had taken on some of the slow serenity that characterized our neighbours, and irritating things such as money or the lack of it had completely receded from our minds.

We had a home, we had all the fuel we needed, and we produced most of our food. The monthly grocery order to the city included only those things which we were unable to grow. Our clothes were

257

replaced when they practically fell to bits. Despite this, we had still not solved the problem of living without money.

"Of course we *do* buy cigarettes and subscribe to some magazines; but even if we cut those out we still have the problem of sugar and flour, tea and coffee. Somehow the idea of getting up in the morning and drinking a glass of cold water is a little too ascetic for my taste."

"Oh, something will turn up," said Jerry easily. "We might try and do some commercial fishing when the season opens. Sell to the packers and make some money that way."

"Or we might raise more vegetables and send them down to the store in return for our grocery order. There are lots of things we can do if we put our minds to work; in the meantime we will just have to be careful."

And so the spring days drifted by while we alternated between spells of activity and idleness. The garden was dug and seeded. The boats were pulled up on the beach for repairs. Working happily in the sun, we recaulked, painted and hammered, pausing now and then to look with satisfied eyes at the glittering sea, the smooth rocks shelving into it and the waving green branches of the cedars. On the beach, a pot of tar and resin bubbled over a small fire and sent out puffs of pungent vapour which blended with the seaweedy smell of the beach at low tide.

On one of our "barking" expeditions, we had discovered oyster beds not far from our property, and one of our daily tasks was to wade out with a pail and a toasting fork and pick off the starfish which preyed on the oysters. Constant supervision kept the pest under control and increased the oyster yield, and in addition, we found that the starfish made excellent fertiliser for the garden.

The salmon run started and with the news that the first blueback had been seen, we were out with our fishing tackle to stand rocking on a sea sparkling with a million diamonds and experience that indescribable thrill that comes when the reel runs out and a fish comes fighting to the surface.

Competition between the islanders was keen and the previous

year we had watched with envious eyes the large fish displayed by members of the mail-day group. This season it was our turn to boast when Jerry came home in triumph dragging a forty-pound salmon. Once again we were the talk of the island, only this time the talk was approving.

"Bigosh, you doing goot," said Hans respectfully.

"Did you catch *it* or did it catch *you?*" grunted Vaino enviously.

"I haff neffer catch one so big," smiled Yonnie, his blue eyes beaming.

We expanded under their praise and began to feel that at last we were on the way to becoming real fishermen.

Keijo, having observed our determined efforts to live life the hard way, relaxed his grim disapproval somewhat, and after inspecting the fish suggested that we salt it down.

Under his supervision, a long session of cutting and cleaning followed. This operation was performed on the rocks by the sea and the pieces of fish laid out in rows. The guts were thrown to the screaming gulls and while Jerry wielded the knife under Keijo's directions, I packed the fish into a stone crock and sprinkled coarse salt between the layers.

When we had finished, we had several gallons of salt fish to lay away for the winter months.

Living up to our resolution of being self-supporting, we made jelly of the wild berries. We canned fish and vegetables and soon had an imposing array of supplies on our storehouse shelves.

We found watercress growing in the little stream that fed the lake. We ate oysters and clams. Faced with our necessity, we shot grouse, and with the vegetables from the garden, the fish we caught and the gifts of "hot" venison killed by our lawless neighbours, managed to live very well indeed.

During the late spring season a cloud of pigeons came to feed on the elderberry trees that grew round the lake. Jerry, wild with excitement, stalked them with the .22 unavailingly for several days, and at last Keijo came to the rescue, pointing out that a .22 was no good for shooting pigeons.

"I lending you shotgun," he said.

This unusual generosity on his part surprised us, but our faces fell when he arrived one day with an antiquated shotgun, some shells and a lot of instructions.

"Don't firing both barrels at once," he warned us as he left.

Once he was out of sight, we looked at the gun. It was old and rusty; one of the hammers was held in place with a rubber band and the gun sights were crooked.

"Gee, I don't think I dare use it," said Jerry, laying it carefully down on the table. "I think I had better stick to the .22."

An hour or so later, the sight of a flock of pigeons flying overhead caused a complete reversal of her cautious attitude, and seizing the shotgun she hastily loaded it and dashed out of the house.

"For heaven's sake, be careful," I warned uneasily as I followed her up the trail to the lake.

We found the pigeons fluttering and cooing in a grey cloud on a tree which was breaking down under their weight.

Jerry took careful aim.

"Remember, only one barrel at a time," I implored.

"Of course, what do you take me for?" retorted Jerry as she pulled the trigger.

Then followed a noise like a dynamite explosion. Both barrels went off. The breach opened up and Jerry fell flat on her back, while the elderberry tree, all its top branches shot away, looked like a disrupted feather bed.

"What on earth happened?" said I, running up to Jerry, who was struggling to her feet in a daze.

"I don't know," she replied, putting her hand up to her head and looking round helplessly. "Did I hit anything?"

"I should say you did," I answered looking round at the debacle; "pigeons, seagulls and elderberries—all made into a salad with one shot. It's a wonder you didn't kill yourself. Whatever made you fire both barrels at once?"

"I didn't!" retorted Jerry indignantly. "I only fired one. The other went off by itself."

"Well! Keijo ought to know better than to lend anyone a gun like that—or perhaps it was meant as a gentle hint that he is tired of having us for neighbours."

"One more bang like that and he *won't* be having us for neighbours," said Jerry grimly. "That gun kicked so hard that I almost found myself looking out of the back of my head."

I picked up the shotgun and together we collected enough shattered pigeons to provide us with breakfast for several days; and a most delicious breakfast it was—pigeon's breast flavoured with elderberry and fried with bacon.

As soon as the winter storms had passed, the weekly mail-day meetings had been resumed and we found ourselves again part of the cheerful group that chatted, gossiped and rocked up and down at the anchorage off the islands.

The fishermen had painted their boats again, repaired them and refitted them for the coming season, and by now were gradually disappearing from among us. Each week the collection of boats that came to meet the mail steamer grew less.

"If you catch an octopus this year, Hans, be sure and bring it back," we told the laughing Dutchman as he made his last trip out before leaving to join the fishing fleet.

"Bigosh, I bring you ze beegest vun in ze Pacific Ocean," he roared back. "You sure you no want to come feeshing wit' me?"

Our commercial fishing project had come to nothing when the fishermen had explained to us the necessity of owning a proper boat and had warned us of the dangers attached to deep-sea fishing unless a person was used to it. The city stores had not been receptive to our plans for exchanging vegetables for groceries, and we had tried to think of other schemes.

My constant searching for ways and means of producing life's necessities had led me to explore the possibilities of manufacturing clothes out of skins, and once after Blackie and Joel had shot a deer that had been raiding their garden, I begged the skin from them and went to work curing it.

The author of our book of general knowledge made up for his

caution in dealing with the art of castration by going all out on the subject of hide curing. There were several methods from which to choose. One recommended the soaking of the hide in water containing various salts. Vaino having frequently impressed on us the fact that the sea contained all the minerals necessary to life, I filled a barrel with sea-water, placed the hide in it and promptly forgot all about it until Jerry's inquisitive pokings about in the barrel led me to investigate the unsavoury contents.

By then most of the water had evaporated, and the hide was green and putrid.

Using a rake, I fished the dripping and malodorous object out and inspected it reluctantly; then, setting my teeth and following further instructions, I pegged it down on a board in the storehouse and proceeded to scrape off the pieces of rotten meat that still adhered to it. The smell attracted clouds of flies and every so often I rushed to bury my offended nose in a pile of fresh clover hay that lay in a corner.

While I gulped, scraped, and endeavoured to avoid breathing, Jerry looked in with a face wrinkled with disgust and hurriedly backed out again.

"Smells like the day of judgment, doesn't it?" she said with a wan smile. "Gabriel, blow your horn and hold your nose."

When the last piece of flesh had been removed, I rubbed salt into the hide and stretched it on a frame to dry. The smell of decaying meat seemed to cling to me all day, and at supper time the sight of baked stuffed cod, platters of vegetables, and fresh raspberry tart left me cold. I looked with nauseated eyes at the food and retreated outside with a glass of water.

The deerskin, spread-eagled on its frame, dried and stiffened till it was rigid and resisted all my attempts to bend it when it was taken off.

Information on the subject of tanning hides was not forthcoming. The Book, having dealt exhaustively with the subject of curing, completely disregarded tanning and went gaily on with a long illustrated list of the many useful articles that could be manufactured out of home-cured skins. For the beginner, mittens of squirrel were shown. Further along the line, as the ambitions of the skin worker progressed, came parkas of arctic fox, and for the advanced pupil, coats of marten and mink.

I put The Book away and went off in search of first-hand information on how to tan a deer hide.

Keijo, when questioned on the subject, turned on the peculiarly aloof expression he assumed when he wished to conceal his ignorance of any subject. The Nelsons solemnly suggested that I try chewing it. I looked at their grave faces, trying to decide whether they were joking or not.

"Eskimos do," commented 'Lias, who, with an apron tied round his broad middle, was rolling out bread dough.

"I'm not an Eskimo," I said, picking up a cookie from a freshly baked batch and biting into it. "Besides, I don't think my bridgework would stand up under the strain."

"You might try and borrow some spare teeth," said Joel idly. "There's a chap over on the mainland who has some real good chompers. He carved them himself out of sheet metal and painted them white. 'Course he only wears them for show, but I reckon they'd be real good for chewing hides."

My last hope, Vaino, burst into roars of delighted laughter at the sight of the iron-hard, partially bald skin standing on its hind legs in the store-room.

"Nobody can say you didn't try," was his sole comment.

Finally, despairing of getting any help from my friends, I nailed the skin to the outside wall of the log house, where it remained, a lasting testimony to my efforts to live life the hard way.

As the weather grew warmer, we frequently took whole days off from our work and packing up a supply of food and a kettle of fresh water, went off for a day's complete holiday.

Our chief haunt was a little white island outside the entrance to the lagoon—an island with smooth shelving rocks running down into a shimmering sea and grey rock walls round which the red, contorted stems of the arbutus trees crawled. The flowers of the arbutus hung down in waxen clusters and the heavy, honey-like perfume floated out over the water to meet us as we rowed towards the shore.

We splashed in the warm rock pools, built fires of driftwood on which we boiled our kettle and, filled with content, lay on the smooth rocks with the sea lapping at our feet and watched the occasional fishing boat chug busily past, or a tug towing a log boom hang seemingly suspended on the horizon.

Another favourite spot was our lake in the woods. Lying on the bracken we spent long silent hours watching a scarlet-crested woodpecker banging resolutely away at an old stump, a kingfisher sitting in white-collared dignity on an overhanging branch, and the dragonflies darting across the still water.

In the interior of the island we found other, larger lakes, lonely and deep, surrounded by a circle of fire-scarred mountains, their shores flaming with bands of purple fireweed. We would slip out of our clothes and step into the cool water, our feet sinking in the soft black ooze round the edge, and strike out for one of the little islands dotting the glassy surface. Here, in the perfect stillness of the summer afternoon, we lay on the moss and baked in the sun till our bodies were tanned to the colour of beechnuts.

The summer wind, blowing off distant snow-fields, rustled among the dry reeds and rippled the surface of the lake, causing the leaves of the spatterdocks round the margin to rock like tiny boats. Around us like faint strains of elfin music floated the native sounds—the sigh of the wind in the tree-tops, the gurgling of water over pebbles and the deep hum of insects.

"Sometimes when we are quiet like this, I feel as if I were on the verge of discovering one of Vaino's great truths," I said, listening to the fairylike symphony, "but somehow it always just escapes me."

"Just as well," answered Jerry lazily. "When you get that far gone, they put you in a strait jacket and stick you behind bars. Don't forget that in this world anyone who departs from the norm is always considered to be mentally unbalanced."

As the summer wore on, small yachts and cruisers on lazy vacations began to anchor outside the lagoon, and their occupants, intrigued by the sight of the turbulent entrance, sometimes rowed in at slack tide in their dinghys to see what kind of freaks chose to live in such an inaccessible place.

We invited them in, and as they sampled our dandelion beer, they cast covert looks round the house.

"Did you really build it yourselves? However did you do it?" And they looked at us as if we were some unusual kind of animal.

In return, we found ourselves invited to lunch on their floating palaces, and in our turn we looked curiously about us at the miniature saloons with their built-in fixtures covered with silver and glassware, the rugs on the floor, easy chairs, and rose-silk-shaded lights. The meals, served by white-coated mess boys, included such luxuries as lobster bisque and ice cream. Accustomed to plain food, we found them rich and unwholesome and frequently ended by turning to the bicarbonate of soda for relief.

"Fair-weather sailors!" sneered Vaino, looking at the lavishly fitted cruisers with contempt. "Notice how they hug the coast and run for shelter whenever there is a breath of wind. They never know the fun of sailing on an open sea with a gale snapping at their heels and the nearest land several hundred miles away."

In spite of his criticism of the visitors, Vaino was always ready to welcome them to his home. We suspected that the opportunity it afforded him to air his views on life was the reason behind the invitation to a giant clambake on his beach.

On these occasions wood for the monster fires was gathered early in the day, and at night the yachts anchored in his horseshoe-shaped bay while their owners gathered jubilantly around the blaze and the smell of steaming clams and hot seaweed mingled with the wood smoke. Laughing and chatting, we sat in a circle, dipping the shellfish into cups of melted butter and drinking the nectar from thick pottery mugs. The big fires of driftwood exploded into showers of sparks which rose high in the air. Beyond the circle of firelight, the sea paced restlessly back and forth, and above us the sky, filled with an eternity of stars, looked down.

When the strangers left, their place was taken by stragglers from the fishing fleet—graceful trollers with tall, raking masts, stubby little gill-netters, storm-battered and weary, all slipping into the lagoon at slack tide like small grey ghosts. Generally they were manned by tired, disappointed men who had had a spell of bad luck and were struggling home with little to eat in their galleys and were faced with the prospect of having to find some other work to see them through the rest of the year.

We took them in and fed them, and they went away with an embarrassed word of thanks, leaving behind as return payment a souvenir in the shape of a salmon spoon or a gaff.

Some of them would stay in the lagoon for a day or two, patching up worn-out engines and insisting that they must be gone on the morning tide; but when morning came and we looked out of the windows, we would see the boats still there, and a little later a wistful-looking fisherman would appear in the doorway murmuring that some vital part of the engine had collapsed and could we give him some fresh water. The invitation to supper that always followed would bring a radiant smile and apologies for being a nuisance.

At supper time our guest would appear, scrubbed to within an inch of his life and shyly bearing a small contribution to the meal from his own scanty supplies—a can of beans or the last of his butter.

In the evening, sitting outside with the sunset flaming over us, we listened to tales of deep-sea fishing told in hesitating and in-articulate sentences that revealed more than the teller realized of the hardships endured.

At dusk, the fisherman would take his leave and return to his boat, and in the cold grey dawn we would be awakened by the rattle of anchor chains and a farewell blast on the horn, followed by the steady pounding of heavy-duty engines leaving the lagoon. Once they were gone we never saw the fishermen again, and the only sign of their passing was the rows of fish spoons and gaffs hanging on the wall.

We fingered them reminiscently. This one brought to mind a

little runt of a man who had distinguished himself by drinking fourteen cups of tea while regaling us with the colourful story of his life. Another conjured up a picture of a burly Scot, his bagpipes tucked beneath his arm, striding up and down the narrow deck of his boat while the peace of Quiet Waters fled, shattered before the banshee wails.

And so summer slipped past without our realizing it until we were suddenly awakened from our enchanted dream by finding September upon us, along with a terse notice from an unsympathetic banker regarding the state of our finances.

Chapter 15

"WE SHALL have to do something and do it quickly," said Jerry, look-ing anxiously at the bank-book. "I think complete bankruptcy is about to set in."

We discussed our problem with Vaino on his next visit.

"You see," I said after we had explained the situation to him, "everything boils down to a question of money. It always does. You can't do anything without it."

Vaino propped himself up against a tree trunk and looked out to sea.

"You think too much about money," he said. "Remember, you have to decide what you want most from life and decide how much you are willing to sacrifice for it."

"I don't know what else we can sacrifice," I said impatiently. "We have cut our living expenses to the bone already."

"I know! I know! Don't think I haven't been noticing the way you have been facing up to life 'the hard way,' as Keijo calls it; but the habits of years are not changed overnight. I think your dream has come to an end. Accept it and remember that you have had eighteen months of perfect happiness; that is more than most people can claim to have had in their whole lives."

I looked at him unhappily. "It was only an experiment anyway. We thought we might be able to make a go of it—at least we tried. I guess we shall have to go back to the city and hope that in a few years we can come back."

Vaino shook his head. "Don't try to come back—it wouldn't be the same again."

"Why wouldn't it? Things here will be just the same."

"Things *here* will be the same, but *you* will change. You have changed already. You are not the same people you were when you first came here."

Vaino straightened himself and picked up his coat.

"It is no use trying to recapture the fascination of a first experince. If you try you will be disappointed. You will go back now and pick up your old life, but the glory of this one will always be with you; and the strange thing about it is that the further you get away from it, the more glorious it will become."

Slinging his coat over his shoulders, Vaino stepped over the gunwale of his boat, touched the engine and shot away down the lagoon towards the entrance. Jerry and I looked after him gloomily.

"I think we always knew it was too good to last," said Jerry. "Vaino is right, of course. All dreams come to an end. Let's face facts now. The party is over and it's time to go."

Realizing that our time was drawing to a close, we plunged into making the most of it. The daily chores were abandoned while we went swimming in the sea with the seaweed and the jellyfish. We walked with Vaino in the still peace of his "chapel," listening to his philosophical discourses. In the evening we drifted home, half drugged with the scent of balsam blown to us from the shore; and when the soft darkness fell our little boat seemed to hang suspended between the starry world above and the drowned reflections below.

The fishermen began to come back one by one to the island and we welcomed them home as each one showed up again at the anchorage on mail days. The season had been a poor one, as was evidenced by the lack of the high spirits that had marked the gatherings of the previous year. Many of the men were making plans for other work to carry them through the winter ahead.

The news that a big industrial development had opened up further north induced many of the fishermen to try for jobs there, and hardly had they returned than they began to disappear again. The boats that gathered behind the rocky islands to wait for the steamer became fewer and fewer until only a handful remained of the usual cheerful crowd that had been used to assemble there each week.

"They will come back," said Irish Pat calmly, lighting his pipe; "they always do. Once a fisherman always a fisherman."

But we knew that we would not be there to see them come back, and in the meantime we missed them. We missed Big Pete, with his handsome Indian face and courteous manner; Magnus, with his wooden leg, and his upper lip packed with "snoose"; and Hans—Hans, who would never come back, for he had been one of the season's casualties and his hearty laugh and long flaxen hair were gone forever beneath the long rolling waves.

One evening Christian and Yonnie came into the lagoon to invite us to go to a dance with them. They were going away, they said, and one of the other men was giving a farewell party for them.

Lively recollections of the last party still present in our minds, we declined; in any case, we were in no mood for parties.

"Everybody is going away," I mourned. "Where are *you* going?"

With shining eyes and happy smiles they explained that they were at last returning to their native lands.

"Then we are not likely to ever meet again," I said. "We are going away ourselves soon."

They murmured regrets in their soft broken English and sailed out of the lagoon and out of our lives.

One by one the links that connected us to our life on the island seemed to be snapping. We began to make preparations for our departure.

Summer's time was running out and the scent of fall was in the air. The heat was going from the sun, and in the blue misty mornings wedge-shaped flocks of geese were seen flying south, leaving one with a strange feeling of loneliness. The plums in Keijo's orchard strewed the ground like a purple carpet, and the hay in the meadow hung festooned from innumerable little wooden crosses, giving the harvested field the sad appearance of a graveyard.

In the evening, the shrill chirping of crickets filled the air, and as we rowed up the lagoon in the moonless night, the phosphorescent water glowed and flashed like living flames. A shoal of fish would dart away before the prow of our boat like a hundred shooting stars, and each time the oar broke the smooth dark surface of the water, a million glowing bubbles rose to the top and drops of liquid green fire ran down the blade of the oar to join them.

Sometimes we talked of our forthcoming departure with Vaino. Of all our friends, he seemed to be the only one who understood our feelings at this time. The others accepted our decision to leave as in the natural order of things; transience was the rule rather than the exception; people came and went and nobody asked any questions.

"Learning to be civilized again isn't going to be easy after this," I said disconsolately; "I shan't be able to forget it."

"I hope you won't," said Vaino serenely. "If you forget, it will mean that your experience here has done you no good."

"I won't forget. When I am back in the city and see buildings and chimneys I will think of how the light is shining on the water up here, and when all I can smell is smoke and gasoline fumes I shall try and remember the scent of pine needles baking in the sun and that will help."

Vaino had found a prospective customer for our property and we had decided to leave the house just as it was in the care of Joel and his brothers until we could make arrangements for the removal of the furniture; and bit by bit we began disposing of the rest of our belongings.

Dizzy Lizzy was sold to the one-eyed Swede to replace his own boat, which had finally sunk. The six hundred feet of water pipe was disconnected and sold to one of the islanders, who was damming up a stream with a view to providing his own house with running water.

Next to go were the hens. Being distinctly useful members of the community, they were spared the fate of becoming a series of chicken dinners and were sold for a good price and carried off in a neighbour's boat to restock a poultry yard robbed of its original occupants by a family of hungry coons.

The empty hen house which we had built with such pride now stood bare and forlorn. The gate hung dejectedly from its hinges and the weeds already began to spring up inside the enclosure.

"It won't be long before the forest takes over again," said Jerry looking at it.

The goats were offered free to anyone who would give them a good home, but there were no takers. They were non-producing animals and pets were a luxury the islanders could not afford.

"You should shooting them," said Keijo. "Goat meat good."

"*Shoot* them!" I echoed, flinging my arms round the billy-goat's neck. "Oh Terry, did you hear what he said?"

In the end, with time running short and our efforts to find a home for them unavailing, they *had* to be shot, and we saw them led away to their fate by 'Lias and Joel.

The end came of the Indian summer—that time of second blooming, with bronze leaves and Michaelmas daisies, with blackberries and plums overripe and juicy, falling from the bough to rot under a misty sun. The time of sweet warm days and cool starlit nights, of quiet shimmering seas and windless skies. Birds flocking south paused to taste the last delights of the waning summer before leaving for gentler climates. Up in the neglected vegetable garden the alders dropped their leaves with furtive whispers and they lay on the ground in a pool of golden tears.

The root-houses of our neighbours were all stocked to the roof with winter supplies; woodsheds were filled to bursting. From the smoke-houses came the pungent smell of burning green alder, and Keijo could be seen hauling his spare boats up the beach out of range of the high winter tides.

Everyone was busy but Jerry and me and the seagulls which swung lazily over our heads.

"It's time for us to go," said Jerry sadly; "there's nothing more for us to do now."

The date of our sailing was set, and the occasion was eagerly seized upon by the islanders as an excuse for a party. Joel and 'Lias came over one morning to discuss the details. The party was to be held at their house and news had already been circulated among the scattered population.

"Nothing doing!" I said firmly. "I haven't forgotten that last little affair at Big Pete's place."

"There won't be any likker at this do," said Joel regretfully. "With so many of the boys away and with Hans and Yonnie gone, all the best stills are closed down."

"How about music?" I inquired. "Who's going to play?"

Joel avoided my eyes and commenced rolling a cigarette in a deliberate fashion, and at last 'Lias said:

"We thought that perhaps—er—you and Jerry? . . ."

I placed my hands on my hips and looked at the pair.

"It always seems to me that at these parties of yours, the guest of honour does all the work. Why should I spend a whole night sawing while the rest of you have all the fun?"

"We can help," said 'Lias hopefully.

"How?"

"I have a banjo."

"Can you play it?"

"No!"

"That's a big help. Any more bright ideas?"

"I can play the mouth-organ," said Joel after a moment's pause.

"Have you got one?"

"No," adding hastily, "but I know where I can borrow one."

"I suppose we could take turns," I said thoughtfully. "Anyway, bring your instruments along tomorrow and we will start rehearsing."

The next day was spent in rehearsing the orchestra. 'Lias and

Joel arrived promptly after breakfast with an air of importance which outrivalled that of any professional symphony performer. Joel had his mouth-organ in his pants pocket and 'Lias carried his banjo wrapped in newspaper.

After much mental anguish, the would-be banjo player succeeded in mastering three basic chords.

"That will do," I told him. "We'll play everything in the same key and if you remember to change the chords in the right place it won't sound too bad."

"What are we going to play?" inquired Jerry, rubbing rosin over the hair of her bow.

I looked at the two men.

"'Rock of Ages,'" said Joel solemnly. "My dad used to sing it."

"Goshalmighty! You can't dance to that."

"'Old Black Joe,'" said 'Lias tentatively.

"Too slow. Don't you know any popular dance tunes?"

After a long and thoughtful pause, Joel came up with "The Isle of Capri" and with that their musical knowledge appeared to bog down completely.

"All right," I said, resigning myself, "we'll play 'The Isle of Capri,' and we'll jazz up 'Rock of Ages' and turn 'Old Black Joe' into a valse and just keep on playing them. Let's try them out now."

'Lias and Joel picked up their respective instruments and we struck the first chord.

Jerry threw her bow down angrily. "I can't play in that key, it's got about sixteen sharps."

I checked with Joel and discovered that the mouth-organ was pitched a fraction below C sharp.

"We can't tune this thing," I said, "it's a fixed pitch. We'll have to tune the other instruments to it, that's all, and you will just have to do the best you can."

Raising the pitch of the banjo to anything approaching that of the mouth-organ strained the strings to breaking-point.

"We had better let them set a little before we force them up any higher; it's no use having them snap—we haven't got any spares."

"Neither have I got any spares," said Jerry. "I'm going to tune down a third and play in another key. It will sound like a barber-shop quartet."

We commenced a new attack on "The Isle of Capri," but after a few bars I laid my violin down in despair. The harder Joel blew, the higher rose the pitch of the mouth-organ and the banjo playing. 'Lias had obviously no ideas at all on when to change from one chord to another, his version of a harmonic accompaniment being to pound enthusiastically on one chord all the way through.

"Oh, this is awful!" I said. "I once heard a German string quartet play a piece of music that had been written in quarter-tones, and it sounded just like this."

'Lias, sweating profusely, unglued his fingers from chord number one and started an uncertain fumbling about for chord number two.

"What's quarter-tones?" he inquired with interest.

I looked at him impatiently.

"Haven't you got *any* idea when to change from one chord to another? Can't you *hear* that when I play the melody, the same chord all the way through doesn't sound right?"

"Sounds all right to me," said 'Lias stoutly.

"Oh come on, come on, let's try it again."

The day of the party brought a new addition to the orchestra when a shabby black fishing boat slid unobtrusively into the lagoon and up to Keijo's wharf, to be greeted with an avalanche of enthusiastic Finnish interspersed with cries of "Lappoleinen! Lappoleinen!"

Some time later, the splash of oars brought us down to the beach. This time it was Sundi and the stranger. They beached their boat and came ashore.

"It is Lappoleinen!" said Sundi as if that explained everything.

"It *is?*" I said, surveying them blankly.

Lappoleinen was nearly as black as his boat. His clothes, so old that they were practically falling off him, were glistening with fish scales and grease; his head was completely bald and encrusted with dirt, but out of his grimy face beamed the Scandinavian's childlike smile and ageless blue eyes.

"How do you do?" we murmured wonderingly.

"He does not speaking only Finn," said Sundi.

We wondered still more.

"He does playing the wi-lin," she explained proudly.

The object of the visit was now apparent. Lappoleinen had brought his violin with him and was all set for an audition.

I looked at Sundi.

"Tell him to play something."

In addition to "not speaking only Finn," Lappoleinen could not "playing from notes"; everything was by ear, and just sufficiently off key to be in no key at all. The fact that there was a string missing on his old ruin of a fiddle was probably a blessing in disguise.

"One string less for him to squeal on," whispered Jerry.

"He will playing with you tonight," said Sundi in the tone of one conveying a great and undeserved honour.

After they had gone I reviewed the situation.

"Things are so bad now that they couldn't possibly be any worse, and if you get enough people all playing wrong notes at the same time, by the law of averages they are bound to hit on a right one once in a while."

Before sundown the fishing boats began to arrive in the lagoon, all ready for the fray. They anchored off the Nelson's wharf with cheerful shouts, and when we rowed up to the house later we found all our friends gathered there to bid us Godspeed.

The big room was a veritable United Nations with its mixture of Scandinavians, Germans and Canadians. There was a pretty young French bride and a scattering of colourful half-breed girls. The kitchen was piled to the rafters with food, and a wash-boiler full of coffee was bubbling on the stove.

Our arrival was the signal to commence.

The "orchestra" went through an elaborate performance which they described as "tuning up," while the guests watched with expressions of mingled awe and respect. Our combined efforts, aided by a large wrench, managed to screw the banjo strings up to within a half-tone's pitch of the mouth-organ; beyond that it refused to go.

Joel ran his mouth-organ across his lips, threw in a few flourishes in a professional manner, spat into the stove, wiped his shirt-sleeve across his mouth, and announced himself as all ready and rarin' to go.

Lappoleinen's three strings had all run down, a fact which did not appear to bother him in the least, and he beamed delightedly round while drawing a scrap of rosin across the greasy hairs of his bow.

'Lias and I had set up a system of nods and winks to indicate when the three different chords were to be changed; and everything being ready, I gave the signal to go and the orchestra plunged gleefully into "The Isle of Capri."

To the Finnish-speaking Lappoleinen, the signal to begin merely meant an indication to play anything that came into his head. Closing his eyes and tucking his violin under his chin, he started off on a sprightly Scandinavian *hambo*.

The nod-and-wink system set up between 'Lias and myself collapsed after the first two chords, and from then on it was every man for himself.

"How'm I doin'?" panted 'Lias, pounding feverishly away on his three chords.

Joel drew a long breath, spat into the stove again, wiped his mouth and said: "I'm kinda dry—let's play something else."

"All right," I agreed, deciding that "The Isle of Capri" had been sufficiently mangled.

"Everybody STOP!" I howled above the din.

Everybody stopped except Lappoleinen, who played happily on until resentful glares from our hosts brought him to a squeaky finish. The dancers stamped and roared their approval and crowded round us clamouring for more.

A brief and useless pause for "tuning up" followed, and we plunged into "Rock of Ages" with Lappoleinen's version of "Life in the Finnish Woods" as an accompaniment. To the dancers, heartily thumping their big boots on the wooden floor, the music was incidental; nobody attempted to keep in step with it.

At intervals Blackie's yells of "Fresh coffee!" caused a distraction and they all fought their way into the kitchen to refuel, after which with fresh gusto they rushed with leaps and howls onto the dance floor again.

Jerry and I, drinking our coffee out of jam jars, the supply of cups having given out, went from one group to another, making our farewells.

There were many gaps in our circle of friends. Keijo and Vaino, of course, never came to these affairs, and the fact that the party was "dry" had proved a good enough reason for keeping Pat away; but there were others. I found myself looking for the golden heads and shy smiles of Yonnie and Christian and listening for the Dutchman's roaring laugh, before remembering with a little pang that they had gone.

At daybreak, the party came to an end. The instruments were put away, the last of the coffee drunk, and the guests began gathering together borrowed cups and spoons and trooping in a hilarious procession down to the wharf. Lappoleinen, his three strings now reduced to two, climbed aboard his old black boat and headed towards Keijo's wharf, where he intended to spend what was left of the night.

'Lias, still nursing his banjo and rotating his three chords, accompanied us down to the float where the fishing boats were hauling in their anchors and casting off their mooring ropes. He helped us untie our row-boat and held it steadily while we climbed in.

"Good-bye now," he said, pushing us out into deep water. "Guess I'll go get me some breakfast—got a long day's work ahead."

We rowed down the lagoon in the cool grey dawn. The smoke was just beginning to rise from Keijo's chimney as we passed his homestead and the early-morning mist was creeping silently over the sea. One by one the boats left the bay; as they passed us, their owners called across the water and waved to us.

"Good-bye, good-bye! . . . Come back some day. . . ."

We watched them sail through the narrow entrance and vanish in the swirling veils of mist.

"I wonder if we shall ever see them again?" I said, straining my eyes to follow them.

The next few days were lonely ones. All our clothes were packed and there was nothing to do but watch the hours slip by and wait for the day when the steamer passed on its south-bound trip. Our neighbours, busy with their preparations for winter, left us to ourselves and Vaino was the only one who found time for a last visit. He chatted casually about the different members of our little community and their affairs, and we all tacitly avoided any reference to our departure. It was not until he was ready to go that I remembered that it would probably be our last meeting.

"Well," he said, standing up, "the tide's on the turn. Any last words?"

I hesitated a moment.

"There's Sarah John," I said. "We can't take him with us and nobody seems to want him." I picked up the cat and stroked his soft fur. "Keijo thinks we should drown him, but you know how I feel about killing things—and he's such a little fellow. Will you give him a home?"

Vaino smiled and took the bundle of grey fluff from me. "I'll look after him." Sarah John, after a bewildered look at me, nestled quietly in his arms.

"That takes care of everything," I said as we walked down to the beach. "The steamer comes down tomorrow. We'll be leaving on it."

"I'll be standing on the beach as you go by," said Vaino. "Look out for me."

I watched him step into his boat, Sarah John clinging to his shoulder.

"We won't be seeing you again before we leave, so I guess I'll say good-bye now."

"Good-bye?" he echoed, smiling his whimsical smile from under his black thatch of hair. "That's an ugly word. There is no need to say that."

"If we never meet again, it's good-bye isn't it?"

Vaino shook his head, and I waited expectantly for the usual philosophical outburst.

"I think you said once that you would always remember the light on the water and the pine needles baking in the sun. Just remember me at the same time and there will be no need of good-byes."

He pushed the hair off his forehead with a characteristic gesture and, taking off his jacket, folded it into a cushion for Sarah John.

"All right, little puss, we're going now."

I looked past him across the quiet lagoon. The sun glinted from behind the clouds and for a moment the rippling waves caught the light and the scent of dry pine needles rose from under my feet.

"I won't forget."

Vaino looked up at the sun-flecked clouds as he slowly drew away from the shore.

"No, you won't forget," he said. "When you have once known beauty, the memory of it is always within you." He looked back over his shoulder, his ugly face full of kindness. "It will stay with you wherever you are."

His engine roared into life and he was gone. I stood for a long time looking after him.

The next day dawned in a flood of early-autumn sunshine. The cedars on the water's edge waved their green skirts in the breeze, and little white-capped waves frolicked on the lagoon.

We had gone to see Keijo and Sundi the previous evening. Keijo had grunted indifferently as we shook hands with him, but there were tears in Sundi's blue eyes as she bade us farewell.

"We'll write to you," I had said a little sadly, already visualizing the one or two enthusiastic letters, and then the gradual lessening of correspondence and the final silence as our ways led us apart.

We had drunk a glass of wine, patted the malemute, and returned to our home filled with gloom.

Now we did the last little things to the house, locked our suitcases, and struggled with groans into city clothes once more. The dogs shook their heads irritably over their leads, and I gasped and fumed inside a leather coat that had grown strangely tight across the shoulders. I looked at Jerry's face shining like polished mahogany above the collar of her white silk shirt, and tried to settle a hat on my riotous and unbarbered hair.

"A fine pair of freaks we are to appear on a city street. We'll probably be picked up as vagrants as soon as we land."

A last look round, and we picked up our suitcases and stepped outside. The door was padlocked behind us, and we loaded our belongings into our remaining boat and pulled away, leaving the log house, empty of life, to sink into a long sleep.

Our last meal was to be eaten at the home of the Nelsons, after which they were to take us out in their boat to meet the steamer. The four men had outdone themselves in an effort to make the meal a memorable one, and the trestle table had been covered with fresh oilcloth for the occasion. 'Lias's cold salmon mayonnaise and hot biscuits would at any other time have aroused an enthusiastic appetite, but this time, Jerry and I picked at the food and fed bits surreptitiously to the dogs under the table.

"Leave us your address," said Joel as we were leaving. "We'll want to keep in touch with you."

We shook hands with Blackie and Sonny, who were not going with us to the steamer; then, following the other two, we made our way down to the float for the last time and boarded the fishing boat.

After the usual amount of cursing and struggling, the ancient engine was kicked into life and we set off. We anchored outside to wait for the steamer and looked at the mountains and the white surf breaking along the rocky coast-line, the drifts of seaweed floating on the surface. We saw a salmon break the water and flash in the sunlight and a baby seal lifted its head from the rocks to look at us.

"I don't feel right in these clothes," said Jerry, wriggling un-easily, "I feel all stuffed up, and my girdle is crucifying me."

"Take it off then," I said unfeelingly, "and let your stockings run down over your ankles."

'Lias and Joel, who had been scanning the horizon quietly, now stood up and prepared to start the engine again.

"Here she comes," said Lias.

Following the direction of his gaze, we saw the steamer. At first it was only a trail of smoke in the distance, then two red smoke-stacks came into view, and at last the complete ship.

The siren echoed among the mountains as she turned in towards us, and the reversed engines set up a swirl of milky water astern.

Joel tossed up our bags and handed the struggling dogs to the deck-hands; then there was only time for a brief handclasp and a word of farewell, and we scrambled aboard. The engine-room bell rang; the engines thudded heavily and we were off.

We stood on deck and watched the fishing boat falling astern and the waving hands of 'Lias and Joel vanish. We watched the scenery sweep past, took our last look at the entrance to the lagoon, the towering mountains at the head and the tumbling white waters of the rapids. Dreaming in the mist behind us were the rocks where we had spent long hours with our friends waiting for the mail.

When we passed Vaino's ghost-haunted beach, we saw a lonely figure standing on the rocky headland. Vaino had kept his word.

Soon after this we came to where tall frowning cliffs and a choppy sea marked the end of the island, and the steamer swung out into the open.

Reluctantly I turned away from the rail.

"Well," I said, heaving a deep sigh, "*that's* all over!"

"Maybe it isn't," replied Jerry after a pause. "Perhaps it's just a beginning. You don't really believe that we will settle down to city life again and forget all this, do you?"

The words struck a responsive note, and in my mind rose a picture of Vaino as I had last seen him, standing in his boat with his eyes fixed on the golden-rayed clouds:

"When you have once known beauty, the memory of it is always within you."

I repeated the words, then smiled reminiscently.

"I wonder on which wall he finds *that* piece of wisdom?"